D1106936

The author at his desk at Green Bank High School where he spent
thirty-two years as teacher of Latin and English.

AFTERGLOW

A Collection of
Short Stories and Poems

The breezes from the mountains
are the breath of freedom.

By W. E. BLACKHURST

McCLAIN PRINTING COMPANY
PARSONS, WEST VIRGINIA 26287

1972

Standard Book Number 87012-127-8
Library of Congress Card Number 72-80632
Printed in the United States of America
Copyright © 1972 by Stella M. Blackhurst
Cass, West Virginia

CONTENTS

Poems

From Hillbilly

WARREN E. BLACKHURST

With the publication of this, the final volume of the writings of the late Warren E. Blackhurst, it is entirely fitting that more should be said about him than has been carried on the dust covers of the previous books by this fine writer. Being an unassuming person, his true worth was often overlooked by the casual observer. A good example of this occurred a few years ago, when Mr. Blackhurst was the official narrator on one of the trips on the Cass Scenic Railroad. At the end of the run, a college student from another state turned to me and said, "That man certainly did a great job of entertaining, and he knows so much about everything we saw. I wonder who wrote it for him." When I informed her that he had no ghost-writer, that he was a highly regarded teacher, dramatics coach and naturalist, and that he was the author of several books, both she and her companion asked where those books could be bought. Later both of them emerged from the Cass Museum laden with copies of every book Mr. Blackhurst had written.

Warren Elmer Blackhurst was born October 10, 1904, in Arbovale, West Virginia, one of eleven children of the Rev. and Mrs. Harry Blackhurst. In 1907, the family moved to Cass, only a few miles distant, only five years after the construction of the great lumber mill and the establishment of the town. It was there that Warren Blackhurst attended elementary school; and it was there, also, where he became acquainted with the day-to-day life of the woodsmen and the mill hands, and the everyday life of a sawmill town. After graduation from the Cass Elementary School, he went to the mill, where he worked for seven years before entering Green Bank High School. Graduating in two and one-half years he entered Glenville State Teachers College in 1928. He graduated from Glenville in 1932. While he was in college he played football, was a member of an undefeated debating team, was the first editor of the student newspaper, and was president of his senior class. Graduating in the depth of the Great Depression, he started teaching English and Latin in the Green Bank High School, from which he had been graduated four years before.

Warren Blackhurst loved to teach. There was no such thing as extracurricular activities. Everything blended together as far as he was concerned. In addition to English and Latin, he taught public speaking, wrote and directed school plays, was class adviser, and yet he found time to develop and teach the first conservation course ever offered in a West Virginia high school. During World War II, when no one else was available, he undertook the football coaching duties; and he compiled the very creditable record of eighteen wins, six losses and two ties. Working with the Greenbrier Ranger District, Bartow, West Virginia, Monongahela National Forest, he developed and put into practice the "Senior Class Memorial Tree Planting Day" at the high school in 1949. Each year, as long as he taught, approximately five acres of seedlings were planted. The project has grown to a veritable forest.

Like many busy men, Warren Blackhurst found time for many things in addition to his teaching in the high school. He was also active in the community and was in demand as speaker or toastmaster at numerous affairs. He and Stella, his wife, were of a small group which determined that the dying town of Cass must experience a renaissance, and they brought into reality their dream of a scenic train to carry tourists, over the old log train tracks, to the top of the great mountain whose crop of timber had brought the town into being. They helped organize the "Country Store" in the building that was once the Company Store; and Blackhurst, who was an expert taxidermist, owned and operated the Cass Museum, where he exhibited mounted specimens of practically every wild creature native to the vast Cheat Mountain area. There, too, can be seen the "tools of the trade" of the woodsman and the mill hand. At the time of his death he was a member of the Pocahontas County Court, elected as a Republican in a county with a high majority of Democratic registrations. He was a trustee of the Cass Methodist Church, and taught a Sunday school class. Occasionally he would occupy the pulpit, in the absence of the minister; but always his first love was teaching. Once he remarked, "I am proud to be a teacher. I am proud of most of my finished products—blossoming of the beautiful and useful lives of my students—just like an artist is pleased with his finished paintings. I never expect to go up in the teaching profession. I don't want to be separated from the classroom and the direct contact I have with my students. When I sit back and think of my greatest accomplishment in life, I am sure it is the fact that my students like Shakespeare and Julius Caesar." Although he had opportunities to go into administrative work, and into college teaching, he stayed with his first love.

But Warren Blackhurst had other loves. He had Stella, who always came first, but he loved nature and the things of nature. Things of the land, the air and the water were a part of his life. He loved nature as it was before the hand of man disturbed it; and he spent much of his life trying to protect it. He liked to fish and hunt, but he liked most just to commune with nature—to learn its secrets and tell them to others—and that became a second life to him. And so, he began to write—to write of those things about which he knew as few people have known them. He was there! He wrote of the first great cuttings of the virgin forests, and in *Riders of the Flood* he told of the formations of the great rafts of logs, from the time they left the stump until they and their riders completed their journey of nearly a hundred miles down the Greenbrier River to the lumber mill at Ronceverte. In *Mixed Harvest* he told of the first timber surveys, the beginning of the sawmill town and the coming of the railroad which would supplant the river as a means of taking the lumber to market. He also told of the people who were there, and those who were drawn to the industry. *Sawdust in Your Eyes* depicts the social life of a lumber town when the twentieth century was young, and no one could tell it better; while *Of Men and a Mighty Mountain* weaves the biographies of the men who made the wheels of the lumber industry turn—from the head of the Company to the mill hand, and how the work of each contributed to the finished product. And through each book there runs a thread of romance, skillfully woven into stories of a great industry. Then there was the railroad, built just for logging, which was the forerunner of the Cass Scenic Railroad.

Before, between and among the writing of his several books, Warren Blackhurst was a prolific writer of articles and stories for magazines. Many of these were based on actual experiences and observations, while some were fiction, often of a humorous vein, but suggested by some happenstance of which he was familiar. When he wrote of fur-bearing animals, of birds or of fish, he did so with the assurance of one who had observed many species in their own habitat, but without their knowledge;

but for any person who was wanton in the destruction of wild game creatures, or their habitat, his wrath was as the wrath of Jove.

And Warren Blackhurst was a poet. Few of his poems were ever published during his lifetime. Often, he wrote only to express his innermost thoughts of the beauties with which nature had surrounded him. It seemed to be a great pleasure for him just to "go forth, under the open sky, and list to nature's teachings. . . ." And yet, he could put an amusing human incident to verse that would bring smiles and laughter to the reader. The publication of selected poems at this time, gives us a better appreciation of the range of this man's ability.

When Warren Blackhurst retired from teaching in 1964, after thirty-two years in the same school, a dedication from the senior class addressed him: "To our friend, confidant and advisor. We have demanded much from you in time and patience. When we needed a helping hand, you were always ready with a word of encouragement. We consider it our good fortune to have been students in your classroom. . . ." It is my regret that I knew Warren Blackhurst only during the ripening years of his life. They were rewarding years for me, and I can understand the sincerity of his students' appreciation of the many things he did for them. He gave them, as Wordsworth expressed it, "that best portion of a good man's life, his little nameless, unnumbered acts of kindness and of love."

The writings of Warren Elmer Blackhurst are a lasting contribution to the literary history of our mountains, and they will be read long after those who knew him are forgotten.

G. A. Bowling

Lewisburg, West Virginia
March 3, 1972

A TRIBUTE—STELLA M. BLACKHURST

Afterglow is my tribute to a very wonderful person, one who gave of himself unstintingly to me, his wife, and to his parents, church, community, school, county and state.

You will find in this book a collection of poems and short stories written by my late husband, W. E. Blackhurst, which I found after his death. In them you will find his love of God and nature along with the tales of the life here in the early part of the century. Humor and pathos run side by side throughout.

He loved the hills of his native state of West Virginia and he saw beauty in everything around him. Through his writings, he wanted to preserve the history of our county for a future generation. He wanted everyone to see the beauty of the hills and know, as he did, the joy of being able to "Lift up mine eyes unto the hills," Psalm 121.

He was a teller of tales, sought out by all who came in contact with him and was genuinely interested in *ALL* people. He had underlined two lines of Rudyard Kipling's poem "IF" as a guide for living:

"If you can talk with crowds and keep your virtue;
Or walk with kings—nor lose the common touch."

I think all his students and friends know that he achieved this.

His ready wit and humor, along with his vast knowledge of this section of West Virginia, made him a popular commentator on the Cass Scenic Railroad. As such he became known and loved by thousands of people.

He often said he was glad he lived in the first part of the twentieth century, a time when so much progress was made. He was also glad he lived in this section of West Virginia. At the time of his death his one request was to be back among the hills he loved. I think Robert Louis Stevenson's "Requiem" is a fitting epitaph for him.

Under the wide and starry sky
    Dig the grave and let me lie:
Glad did I live and gladly die,
    And I laid me down with a will.
And this be the verse you grave for me:
    Here he lies where he longed to be:
Home is the sailor, home from the sea,
    And the hunter home from the hill.

xiii

A DEPARTED FRIEND

There are times when each of us reflects on days gone by and remembers persons who have influenced our lives in myriads of ways. It is at such times that Warren E. Blackhurst is fondly remembered by his many friends and former students as an outstanding example of a man who was always ready with a smile, a handshake and words of wisdom and encouragement. "Tweard" was a man of many and varied talents who was a friend to the rich and poor—the important and the common-place—the worthy and the unworthy. He was foremost a philos-opher. Many times have I listened to his philosophy in the classroom; while working with him in the fields of his beloved farm or while sitting far into the night as he prepared specimens for his magnificent collection of mounted animals. "Tweard's" philosophy seems to me to have been a simple one. Basic to his every thought was an honest regard for his fellow man and a deep and genuine respect for God and for all nature. He was a conservationist in the best sense of the word. He taught and practiced conservation and instilled the principles of conserva-tion in all with whom he had contact. As a teacher he was without equal. Hundreds of young people were given their first real introduction to literature, Latin, public speaking and acting under his tutelage. We have departed his classes not only wiser in subject matter but much wiser in the art of living. "Tweard's" ability as an author needs no extolling here. His books dealing with life in the early lumbering days in and around his hometown, Cass, are well known and widely read and acclaimed. They have preserved for future generations the people and deeds of an interesting and important period in our history and have added immeasurably to an understanding and knowledge of that period. Most of all "Tweard" is remembered as a friend who has made our lives easier and better through his humor and wisdom.

Roy Clarkson
Department of Biology
West Virginia University
Morgantown, West Virginia

xv

ACKNOWLEDGMENTS

I would like to express my gratitude to all my friends and family for their assistance in the publication of this book.

I would especially thank the following people for their help with the script and pictures. Mr. and Mrs. G. A. Bowling, Mr. and Mrs. William Powell, Mr. and Mrs. Ivan Clarkson, Mr. and Mrs. Carl Davis, Eugene Burner, Gene Crist, Pocahontas County Historical Society, Mr. and Mrs. Richard Brockway, Elmer Burris, Richard Carter, Edward J. Wojas, Wayne Cox, and Duard H. Estep, Ph.D., minister, First Baptist Church, Elkins, West Virginia.

The painting for the dust jacket was copied from a slide taken by the author, W. E. Blackhurst. I deeply appreciate the work done on this by our friend John C. Davis, who also painted the pictures for the dust jackets of *Mixed Harvest* and *Of Men and a Mighty Mountain*.

I want to thank the editors of the following—*West Virginia Hills and Streams*, *West Virginia Hillbilly*, *Natural History of the Cass Scenic Railroad*, and the *Charleston Gazette* for allowing me to use the stories and articles printed in them. I felt these were worthy of being published in a book.

Stella M. Blackhurst

****

THE PLANTING OF "PRUNY" O'LANNEY

There had been no real need to bury Sam Given so quickly. Still there was no need to keep him any longer. He was thoroughly dead at five o'clock in the morning. The feed store proprietor and impromptu undertaker had a ready-made casket that fitted the body. So since the weather was suitable and Sam had no family to delay things, he was safely buried before five o'clock in the evening.

Sam had been brought into Sawdust Pile from one of the camps. Out there a lodged tree had given way unexpectedly and crushed the sawyer. Doc Giles had pronounced his case hopeless upon arrival at his office.

When Doc said a man was going to die, he usually did. Therefore, it wasn't strange that before Sam's body was cold, four hicks were busy shoveling out a grave down at Dead Man's Elbow. Nor was it out of the ordinary, when at four in the evening, Mitch Wiggins's dray wagon rounded the sharp angle of road that gave the graveyard its name. There the hands of sturdy wood hicks lifted Sam's mortal remains from the wagon. Thirty minutes later a crude cross of unpainted wood marked the last resting place of Sam Given.

At seven o'clock that evening the lobby door of the Logger's Roost pushed open. Into the room walked "Pruny" O'Lanney the only man in the cuttings that might have been called a close friend of Sam.

By some quirk of fate taciturn, grouchy Sam had been drawn to the talkative, quick witted Irishman. "Pruny" in turn had found the stolid Sam strangely to his liking. Over the past years the unusual attachment had resulted in many escapades together. Adventures indeed, in which Sam might never have found himself had it not been for the more daring and fun loving Irishman.

"Pruny" had gotten his name from one of his more daring customs. In camps where intoxicants were strictly taboo on pain of immediate firing, he had found his thirst unbearable. To slake that thirst "Pruny" had invariably formed an alliance with the camp cook. Prune juice carefully saved from the ever

1

present dish of the log camps was doctored with yeast under the skilled direction of the wiry little teamster. When it was "right" according to "Pruny," it would "make a chipmunk bate hell out of a wildcat."

It was likely that such illicit activity in time became known to the bosses, but "Pruny" was never fired. Even a hard-drawn rule could be winked at in the case of a man who was a born wizard with horses.

"Pruny," little and wiry though he was, could handle the biggest and most spirited team with a skill that was near the miraculous. From any team in the woods he could get more work than any other teamster. And, equally as important, he never crippled or killed a horse. He was uncanny about spotting danger ahead and keeping his horses out of it.

When "Pruny" entered the lobby, he was as near dressed up as anyone had ever seen him. He still wore his cork shoes but otherwise he was changed. Customary snagged off dirty trousers had been discarded for a pair of heavy gray wool. These were new. A shirt of white silk, the worse for time, took the place of his usual checked "Richie." A flaming red necktie competed for honors with his fiery round nose. Reaching to halfway between his hips and knees he wore a huge black coat made in the manner of those worn by the clergy. His head was bare and the bald spot shone with a scrubbed brightness.

"Pruny" made his way solemnly to the back of the lobby. There he placed the old carpetbag he carried carefully on the floor. With a bandana he mopped his bald head as he addressed the proprietor.

"Top o' the evenin' to ye, Mike," he greeted. "Oi've come to be wakin' me friend, Sam. Ye could be tellin' me where they're kapin' his body." Mike Rann was startled. "You've come for what?" he demanded.

The dozen or more loggers present fell quiet. "Pruny" explained with patience. "Oi've come to be wakin' Sam Given. Sure, and it's a wake they'll be havin'. There's no man departs this world that's no desarvin' of the last respects of a wake, least o' all me friend, Samuel Given."

Mike scratched his jaw and stared helplessly at the quaint figure before him. A hick volunteered to answer, "Why, I hate to tell you, 'Pruny,' but no one knowed you was comin', so we buried Sam this evening."

2

"Pruny" sat down and stared at the faces that had now surrounded him. He seemed to be looking for signs of a joke on their faces. Each face was honestly sympathetic.

"You see, 'Pruny,' " Mike explained, "there was no family to claim the body and no one could see any reason to keep him. We didn't know you was comin' in. We buried him down at Dead Man's Elbow."

"'Tis sad," he muttered, "a sad affair. No wake. No proper honors to the dead. Not a friend to spare the time o' one night for doin' his remains due honor." "Pruny" shook his head in sad bewilderment.

"If I'd knowed you was comin', I'd a told 'em to keep him," volunteered one huge logger, "and I'd a set up with him to keep you company."

Again "Pruny" shook his head. "'Tis no good now to make excuses. Poor Sam is in his grave, may the saints presarve him! There's no thing we can do for him now."

After a long moment of silence he again spoke, "Bedad! it may be for the better. What with the solemn chap auld Sam was maybe he would no take to havin' us whoop it up around his mortal carcass."

"You're mixed ain't you, 'Pruny,' " asked Mike. "I never heard of no whoopin' it up at any wake I ever attended."

"Pruny" glared. "And would ye be settin' around like a gang o' unhappy buzzards? Would ye tiptoe across the floor for fear o' the dead man awakin'? Would ye be talkin' in whispers so low the poor bye could no hear what ye'r sayin'? Divil a wake ye'd have with no fun to keep things a movin'."

The crowd gaped and Mike asked feebly, "You mean you'd have a party?"

"Pruny's" anger subsided. Slowly he nodded. A reminiscent look came into his bright blue eyes. "Me byes," he said quietly "'tis a month o' me wages I'd be givin' just to be back in Auld Kilarney and go once more to pay respects to an auld departed neighbor."

Here "Pruny" fished from his pocket his battered corncob pipe. With blue smoke curling around his head he continued. "Me, byes, ye know not what a party is if ye've no been to an auld time wake in good Auld Ereland. Why many's the toime Oi've seen food and drink stacked higher than the casket! And

3

bonnie lassies all around to press the vittles on ye. And nary a soul no thought to leave 'til mornin' sun's upon ye."

"Sound more like the fixin' for a dance than a wake," someone suggested.

"Aye, me lad!" Old "Pruny" answered, "and a dance it was. A jig runnin' full o' the night that'd wear out the shoes upon ye."

"Too bad we missed it," laughed Mike. "Maybe we could dig Sam up and have one yet."

"Divel have ye fer such a thought," answered "Pruny." "Once a man be in his grave there he stays 'til the judgement. There'll be no wake fer poor auld Sam, but," here his blue eyes twinkled, "I see no harm at all if we'd have a sip in his honor."

"Pruny" bent down and threw open the carpetbag. In it among a few shirts used for packing, the crowd saw four quart jars. "Pruny" lifted one and turned to Mike with the dignity of a deacon. "Mr. Rann would ye be so kind as to furnish us with some glasses?"

When Mike hesitated, Lank Barr spoke in his usual solemn voice, "Jeff Muldoon is out of town. The arm of the law won't be interferin'."

Mike produced the glasses. As "Pruny" filled them he stated, "No prune juice me lads! No prune juice here, but the best o' Lank Barr's concoction. And so ye all know Lank's the master o' all the moonshine masters."

When each glass was filled and handed around, "Pruny" held his own aloft. "To me friend, Samuel Given, saints rest his soul. Drink, me byes, to a good man now departed."

"Pruny" drained his glass. All drank except Lank Barr, the capable moonshiner. This caused no comment for all knew that Lank was a teetotaler. He made it and sold it but never drank.

"Pruny" wiped his bristling gray mustache and watched the slower drinkers. "'Tis strong as lye, me lads," he said, "but it'll put the feel o' life within ye. Don't be timid, lads. There's more in the bag." Then bowing to an imaginary person he asked, "Mr. O'Lanney, will ye be havin' another?"

Mr. O'Lanney would, and before some finished one glass, "Pruny" had swallowed a second.

One drink called for another. The generous "Pruny" kept the glasses filled and never ceased talking. Greater and greater became the wakes that he had formerly attended. The mountains

4

of food became whole mountain ranges and the bottles of drink increased to ocean like proportions.

"Pruny" grew mellow. His Irish brogue rolled off his tongue like liquid honey. Every man present became his beloved brother. Then with increased drink the inevitable happened. "Pruny" grew sentimental. His thoughts returned to Sam Given.

"Saints defend auld Sam, me ever lovin' brother. Poor neglected Sam with not a soul to be wakin' him. Pushed from sight benathe the earth his body's cold." Here "Pruny" glared around at the crowd. "And it's me last shirt I'll bet, ye dug his grave too shallow." He shook his fist and continued. "Aven now at this very minute the mutts and mongrels o' Sawdust Pile may be faisting on his carcass."

One who had helped dig the grave hastened to explain. "No, 'Pruny,' we dug her deep. They was a good two feet o' earth above the rough box."

"Pruny" howled like a dog in pain. "Two fate o' airth, he says. Two fate o' dirt bedad. And ye say auld Sam was buried. Buried, indade! Ye no more than sprinkled the airth upon him. Buried ye say! Two fate of dirt! A buzzard may scratch through that with a flit or two of his tail feathers."

"Pruny" swallowed the last drops in his glass as though filling up with new powder. But when he set the glass down, his outburst had subsided. He spoke with quiet impressiveness.

"Listen me lads, I'll be askin' ye all one favor." He stopped and looked from face to face. Most of them nodded.

"Pruny" continued, "Some day, me byes, and maybe soon Auld Nick must have his earnin's. 'Pruny' O'Lanney'll have to go to answer at the jidgment. Promise me, lads, if there's men among ye, when the day arrives, ye'll give me a decent plantin'."

Mike answered, "Sure, 'Pruny,' we'll see you put away decent. How do you want it done?"

"Pruny's" forefinger, calloused from holding harness lines, jabbed into Mike's belly. "Get pencil and paper Mike, me friend, I'll want it down in writin'."

While Mike secured writing material the others crowded around "Pruny." They had drunk enough to make them ready for anything.

A tall logger jokingly addressed the little Irishman. "When you die, 'Pruny,' we'll dig your grave ten feet deep."

With a quick motion "Pruny" turned to Mike who was returning with the paper. "Ye hear that, Mike? Ye hear the man promise? Ten fate he says he'll put me down, where even Auld Nick won't think me worth the trouble of exhumin! Ye hear him Mike, me friend. Jest put that down on paper."

Mike began to write and "Pruny" began again, "Now, ye listen, lads! When 'Pruny' kicks the bucket, on that very day, see that ye fix my body. Dress me in a white silk shirt with a necktie red as blood or redder. A long black coat I'd like to be havin' like this O'im now a wearin'. As for pants, no pryin' soul will see 'em so it rally does no matter. Give me pants or give me none. I'll no argue that matter."

"Now wait a minute, 'Pruny,'" said a voice from the group. "You can't go flittin' around the next world without any trousers."

"Pruny" considered. "'Tis right ye air. No man knows fer sure where he's goin'. O'Lanney might wake up with a pack o' female angels. Ye'd best put on me britches."

"Pruny" stopped to fill his pipe. Then after a pause continued. "As to shoes, Oi know 'tis not custom but Oi'll be planted in me cutters. Me fate would niver feel right with no corks benathe 'em."

"Pruny" took his old cob pipe from his mouth and held it toward them. "Ye've seen me all me life with this," he said. "Stick her atween my teeth as soon as Oi'm dead and watch Oi don't bite yer fingers when Oi be snappin' at it."

"How about the wake?" asked Mike.

"Pruny" answered. "Jest simple, Mike, me friend, jest ye make it simple. Lay me out in the lobby here where me best o' friends will gither. Load a table over there with food in plenty. For that Oi'll be payin' before Oi depart. And, Lank Barr, me lad, come hither."

"Pruny" pulled a stuffed wallet from his pocket and extracted two twenty-dollar bills. "Here, Lank, ye auld moonshine master, ye're paid in advance to furnish liquid refreshment fer me wakin'."

Lank protested in his slow speech. "Naow, 'Pruny,' I jest cain't take it. I may pass out long afore you do."

"Pruny" pushed a finger against Lank's lean belly. "Lank, ye'll niver die. The divil don't want ye. Ye'd be too much

6

competition fer his Satanic Majesty." And "Pruny" thrust the bills into Lank's pocket.

"Pruny" now shook a solemn warning finger. "See to it that ye git a good fiddler. One that knows his tunes. Not one o' them as sounds like a boar hog scratchin' himself on a sliver o' wood. And be sure ye'll invite the ladies. Divil a bit o' good a wake may be with no ladies to make things romantic."

"How long shall we hold the party?" asked Mike who was busy writing.

"How long?" roared "Pruny." "How long indade? Ye'll be startin' at fall o' darkness. With the music playin' fit to kill and food stacked on the table. The laddies'll swing the colleens around like bubbles on the water, and Lank's moonshine will flow as free as Auld Kilarney's fountains. When the sun rides high ye'll no go home but take me straight to the Elbow."

So carried away was "Pruny" by his own directions that he danced a few steps to imaginary music.

"How do you go to the Elbow?" Mike interrupted.

"The only way a dacent man should go," answered "Pruny." "All me life Oi've driven horses. To me grave Oi'll go pulled by horses. But mind ye! No poky creepin' will there be in the percession. Ye'll lay the whip across their rears. Ye'll kape them movin'. Ye'll take auld 'Pruny' to his grave as fast as horse flesh can travel."

Mike scratched his head. "I never saw a procession like that," he said.

"Then," answered "Pruny," "ye'll be seein' sights ye niver saw afore. And, too, Oi'd like it if ye'd all oblige me, that a good gang o' ye byes might go ahead in proper vehicles to announce me comin'. Plenty o' noise and plenty o' speed so folks'll know we're passin'. And listen ye well. Nary a sniffle nor nary a tear let me see or hear from amongst ye. When ye git back from that trip, me lads, ye'll say ye've been to a rale plantin'."

"Pruny" mopped his shiny head where beads of sweat were standing like dew drops. "Now, Mike, me friend, let's hear what ye have written."

Mike worked busily for a few more minutes. Then clearing his voice he read, "We, the undersigned, agree that when 'Pruny' O'Lanney dies we'll dress him in cork shoes, any old britches, silk shirt, red necktie and long black coat. We'll hold a wake for

7

him with food, drink and dancing. We'll take him to his grave as fast as horse flesh can travel and we'll bury him in a grave ten feet deep."

"Fine," said "Pruny," "but ye be fergettin' me pipe. Add a line if it plase you."

Mike added "P.S. Corn cob pipe in his mouth." And "Pruny" nodded approval.

Mike Rann and fourteen others signed the paper.

Two years of sunshine and shadow passed over Sawdust Pile. Few changes were made in the physical features of the town as a whole. There were none in Hell's Acre. But the eddying back-water of humanity itself saw many changes. Old faces were seen no more; new ones took their places. Some of those who had enjoyed "Pruny's" hospitality and moonshine had moved on; others had preceded him to Dead Man's Elbow. Nearly all had forgotten the compact they had entered into, or had disregarded it.

Then one night in early May the log train came in with a different burden. On a makeshift cot in a supply car lay "Pruny" O'Lanney. He was down with pneumonia.

They carried him to the Logger's Roost and there Mike made him comfortable. "We'll get him to the hospital on the morning train," one of the cot carriers said, but "Pruny" shook his head.

When the others were gone, "Pruny" reached for Mike's hand. "Mike!" he said in a husky voice between gasping, "ye remember don't ye, Mike, the paper we was after signin'?"

Mike nodded, "Sure, 'Pruny,' but you'll be all right. Why in a few days—."

But "Pruny" was shaking his head. "No, Mike, 'tis me finish. And if ye'll first tell me ye'll kape yer word, Oi'll be a goin' quite happy."

And Mike answered, "I'll see to everything, 'Pruny.' "

"Pruny" pointed to his clothing which had been deposited on a chair. "Me wallet's in me pants. There'll be plenty fer payin' the piper." At five next morning "Pruny" died.

That was a busy day for Mike Rann but he went to his task with a vengeance. By nine o'clock he had located six of the fourteen men who signed "Pruny's" agreement. Three more were in camps and would be in by early evening. No others could be found. Those present set to work on all arrangements.

Sawdust Pile never guessed what was in the making. If the

8

citizenry saw any funeral arrangements they seemed only of the ordinary sort. But working quietly the funeral committee was preparing a sight that Sawdust Pile would never forget.

Just after dark that night the casket of "Pruny" O'Lanney was carried into the lobby of the Logger's Roost. "Pruny" had never assumed more dignity. He was dressed in new clothes. High cutter shoes with gleaming sharp caulks were concealed by the lower half of the casket but the upper half laid back disclosed his upper part in all its glory. His silk shirt gleamed in crinkly newness and the flaming red tie seemed about to burst into flame. A long coat of black satin gave a contrasting look of solemnity and seemed to frown upon the gay shirt and necktie. Even "Pruny's" nose had been rouged to maintain its natural lustre. The newness ended with his clothes. Clamped between his teeth was the same blackened corncob pipe that "Pruny" had smoked for years.

At one side of the lobby a long table was filled with food. There were sandwiches of every description. Fruits that could be obtained were piled upon platters. Cakes, pies, roasts of meat and various makes of cookies were placed about in no arrangement or order.

As twilight fell, Lank Barr had entered. He went straight to a back room and returned very shortly. His brief visit assured the others that his share of refreshments were ready.

Shortly after dark the wake began to assemble. Mike and nine of the compact signers were present. Several loggers who had known "Pruny" were present by invitation or by just voluntarily coming. White Wing and Big Susie, their palace of sinful delight closed for the night, came in bringing three of their girls. Four other women appeared, two of them residents and two traveling ladies.

The wake began with a strained sobriety. The guests ate and talked with an occasional visit to the back room where Lank Barr had left his contribution. With each visit there the sobriety wore thinner so that when Mack Floe and Jim Jarvis came in at ten bringing fiddle and guitar, the guests were ready for dancing.

The memory of that wake will last for many a decade. Needless to say there was little sleep for that part of Hell's Acre. From ten to five in the morning the music seldom ceased and

9

the tramping of the dancers shook every room in the ungainly old structure.

When at 1:00 a.m. Jeff Muldoon entered and demanded quiet, Mike shoved the compact under his nose and informed him the dancers were carrying out a dead man's wishes. The thought of a dead man's last request awed Jeff no less than the hostile looks of the crowd and he left in considerable confusion.

The dance never slackened until after two. At that time a few who were tiring started two poker games which continued until morning. Over a thousand dollars changed hands at one of the tables.

Those who had the stamina were still dancing at daylight. Ruby Walls, one of White Wing's girls, had worn out both shoes and was still going strong barefooted. When two woodsmen vied for her as partner in the next dance, a fight broke out. It was settled quickly. Massed manpower pitched both into the street with a stern injunction to be respectful in the presence of the dead.

At five o'clock with daylight breaking the music ceased and all fell silent. Hell's Acre sighed with relief and prepared for some late sleeping.

At seven o'clock the sleep was rudely shattered. A wagon drawn by two spirited horses drew to a stop before the Logger's Roost. Behind it Mitch Wiggins's dray pulled by old Barney also drew to a rattling halt. Immediately the double doors of the lobby opened and six sturdy hicks, lacking all the sobriety of customary pallbearers, carried out the casket of "Pruny" O'Lanney. Behind the six came all revelers who had attended the wake.

With the expected squeals from the women and the loud talk from the men, the big front wagon was loaded with mourners. At the same time the black casket was being loaded into Mitch's old dray. With "Pruny" safely in the wagon feet forward the pallbearers were starting for places in the forward vehicle when one of their number halted them.

"Wait a minute, boys," he called. "This ain't right."

When all stopped and looked askance, the speaker continued, "Old 'Pruny' wouldn't feel right with someone else drivin'. He should hold the lines."

"But he can't drive now," answered another.

"Old Barney'll foller tother wagon," Mitch offered helpfully.

10

Without further ado a packing case was procured. Two men lifted the head end of the casket to as nearly a vertical position as safety would permit and the packing case was placed behind it for support.

"Me and Jed'll ride here and hold it steady," one man offered.

The lid of the casket was laid back and the harness lines quickly wrapped around "Pruny's" stiff hands. Mitch crouched low in the front of the wagon bed whip in hand. The four pallbearers, not holding to the casket, remained on the back of the wagon.

Seeing all ready, Mike Rann, from the foremost wagon, yelled, "Remember your contract! Fast as horse flesh can travel. Let's go!"

The forward driver shouted, "Get up" and laid his whip across the backs of the team. The horses leaped into a gallop jerking the packed wagonload of yelling humanity over the rutted roadway.

Mitch Wiggins brought his long hickory switch down over sleepy old Barney's rump and yelled loudly. With a startled grunt the old dray horse leaped forward. The four pallbearers standing in the rear were jerked to the floor of the wagon but the two holding the casket, thus braced, managed to keep their feet.

Encouraged by Mitch's flailing whip old Barney dashed after the other wagon. Those in the forward group yelled approval. With a hundred feet separating them at the start, the two wagons thundered through the main roadway of Hell's Acre. As they crossed the steel arched bridge with its rattling plank floor, old Barney had cut the lead to fifty feet. The spirit of the race was upon him.

When the two wagons lurched crazily over the rough railway crossing, only a scant twenty-five feet lay between them. As they thundered into the main street of Sawdust Pile, the old dray horse was nosing the rear of the front wagon.

The noise of the cortege carried far ahead and all the townspeople had time to line the roadway or peer from open doorways. Some stared in stupefied amazement and then asked neighbors what had happened. Others ran for shelter, thinking the whole thing a double runaway. Four women claimed to have fainted at the "awful spectacle."

11

Miss Emmaline long described the "awful spectacle" graphically. "The first wagon came at such speed you'd think old Nick was driving it. There must have been a hundred men packed on it, not to mention them disgraceful hussies. They was all yelling like Satan's demons. But that was nothing, mind you. When the next wagon passed, I don't know why I didn't faint. There was that 'Pruny' O'Lanney a standing right up in his coffin, and a cracking that whip over the horse. He was laughing, I tell you. I could hear him. And some said smoke was coming from his pipe! I say it was fire! The flames was shooting right out of that old pipe or I'm a liar. I always said that 'Pruny' O'Lanney was in league with the Devil and now I guess that proves it."

Leaving a thunderstruck populace behind, the funeral train raced down the roadway toward the graveyard. As they neared the sharp bend of road, that gave the place the name of Dead Man's Elbow, the forward driver pulled hard on his horses. His slowing process also slowed old Barney. Both men who were holding the casket braced themselves hard against the turn and managed to hold "Pruny" upright. Thus the turn was made without accident and the horses drew to a panting halt by the graveyard.

When the badly shaken pallbearers had closed the casket and carried it to the high mound of clay that loomed there, they found that another of "Pruny's" last requests had been honored. A grave of full ten feet depth yawned darkly at the feet of the Reverend Sampson, who, book in hand, stood waiting. A frown of angry disapproval marked the preacher's stern features. However, enough explanation of the strange requests of the departed had been given that he consented to hold the graveside service for which he had been summoned.

At the conclusion of the brief service a new difficulty presented itself. The customary lowering straps were not long enough to allow the casket to reach bottom.

"We can't jist drop him," one pallbearer remarked. " 'Pruny' wouldn't like that."

"Nope, he'd git up and cuss you," another replied.

Mike was already correcting the difficulty. He was removing the long harness lines from Barney's bridle. With their length added to the coffin straps "Pruny" was safely lowered.

That afternoon Jeff Muldoon, driven by outraged citizens, summonsed all the mourners who could be identified to Mayor

Dolan's court. All the mourners came whether they had received a summons or not. All Sawdust Pile came for that matter. In fact, there was such a crowd present that Mike Rann announced regretfully, "If we'd knowed such a mob was to show up we could a sold tickets."

When Mayor Dolan charged the group with disorderly conduct, Mike solemnly laid the agreement before him. His Honor read the scrawled words and signatures and scratched his head in perplexity.

"We was only fulfillin' a dead man's request," Mike announced. "They ain't no law been wrote against it."

Seeing the confusion of the mayor, Jeff Muldoon came forward and whispered in his ear. Dolan nodded happily.

"Guess I can't hold you on disorderly conduct," he announced, "but there's a town ordinance that provides for a five-dollar fine for anyone drivin' faster than a walk over the big bridge. That means each driver is fined five dollars."

Mike laid five dollars on the mayor's table. "That's the last five he left me to pay expenses. It'll pay for the first wagon. 'Pruny' was drivin' the second one. You can collect from him down at the Elbow."

****

REVENGE IS SWEET

Old Andy Stiles rolled out of his bed early that November morning of 1884. He hated to leave the warm comfort of the cornhusk mattress but there was work to do.

With a grim, set face the old man went about the task of preparing breakfast. Fat side meat soon sputtered in the skillet and the battered coffee pot bubbled a cheerful song. It was the only cheerful sound in the littered cabin.

As he sat down to his hastily prepared breakfast, Andy muttered, "Cain't kill a varmint on a empty belly."

The meal ended, the old man took down a shiny 32-40 rifle from its pegs on the wall. The gun was the only well kept thing in the cabin. As he counted out half a dozen cartridges from a box, Andy said to himself with an apologetic air, "Course I only

13

need one but mebbe I'll see some critter fer meat on the way back."

Snow was falling thickly and the predawn air was cold as Andy cut through the woods toward Jacob Run. "Should hev it over an' be back in a hour or so," he thought.

It was still dark when Ben Elder's cabin on Jacob Run came into view. There was a light in Ben's cabin. "Old devil's up airly," Andy muttered. "Nothin' like gittin' a airly start on yer dyin' day." With that pleasant thought he quickly crossed the small clearing that surrounded the house and crouched behind a short section of stone wall. The wall, started by Ben over a year ago flanked only one side of the planned enclosure. From its protection both front and rear doors could be seen.

This was to be Ben Elder's "dyin' day." Andy had decided the matter yesterday. Too long already he had endured the rankling memory of what had happened a month ago. Bad enough it was that Ben had shot one of Andy's hogs and refused to pay for it. To add insult to injury Ben had dogged the remaining razor backs home and informed Andy that this was a mere beginning. Next time the hogs invaded the Elder corn patch all would be summarily shot and butchered.

"Lot o' hogs he'll butcher atter today," thought Andy. "This time tomorry he'll be a dancin' on Beelzebub's coals."

It was cold behind the wall. Andy shivered and buttoned his old jacket tightly around his throat. Ben would be out soon. He'd have to come out to feed his cow.

Full daylight came in an increased downfall of snow. It was borne by a keen wind that cut deep into Andy's shivering body. It was hard to watch the doors from the small peephole between the rocks. The wind seemed to find that same opening and its sting kept tears in the eyes of the intent watcher.

An hour after daylight the grim watcher behind the wall jumped. There had come a shout from the log cabin. "Hey, Andy. How is it out thar? Ain't cold be ye?"

Thunderstruck old Andy couched lower. His sense of guilt at the sound of his enemy's voice unnerved him. His hands shook and his eyes went wildly about in search of an avenue of escape.

As if reading his mind, Ben called again. "Nary chanct ter run fer it. I'd pick ye off fore ye made ten jumps. Jist git yerself settled. Ye'll be right thar till dark."

Andy answered nothing. He couldn't have spoken. The dread

14

position in which he found himself rendered him speechless. With deep certainty he knew what Ben said was true. From his window Ben could be master of the situation. Should Andy attempt to run or even raise his head above the wall Ben would kill him.

The voice came again. "Ye'll find a nice soft rock to set on, Andy. Make yerself to home. That is onles'n ye want ter stick yer head up. I got the hull wall kivered."

Throughout the long morning Andy sat glumly against the stone wall, his rifle gripped firmly and ready. At intervals Ben called a cheery few words from the cabin. Andy never answered. "Mebbe the old hawg thief is jist bluffin'. Mebbe he dunno fer sartin I'm hyar," he thought hopefully. But that was mere hope. Ben had seen him and knew he was there. The bluff idea gave no encouragement to a half frozen watcher.

About noon a blue jay alighted on top of the wall at the lower end and cocked an inquisitive head at the forlorn figure behind it.

"See that air jay?" called Ben's voice. A rifle cracked at the cabin window and the jay dissolved in a cloud of feathers. Andy pressed closer to the protecting rocks.

"Gonna be a powerful cool afternoon," Ben called. "An' the moon on that new snow is goin' ter make the airly part o' the night like daytime. Be atter midnight afore ye kin light out. Got airy bit o' food with ye?"

Andy shuddered. There would be a moon and the snow was stopping. There'd be good vision tonight.

"Tell ye what, Andy," Ben called. "I don't hanker ter hev ye freeze on my proppity. Make ye a bargain. I jist take that hawg I shot ter pay fer the corn the bunch et. Ye agree ter keep yer corn stealers to hum hereafter and I'll let ye come out from behind them rocks. If ye want it thet way stick yer hat up on your rifle barl an' wave it."

After a wait of half an hour during which Ben kept a close watch on the wall, a battered old hat rose slowly from behind the rocks. It waved feebly.

"Come on in," shouted Ben.

When he noticed that the stumbling figure had left the rifle behind the wall, Ben went out to meet him. There was real solicitude in the manner in which the half frozen man was helped into the cabin.

15

Old Andy spent a glum hour "thawin' out" by his enemy's fire. At the end of that time he spoke for the first time. "Reckon ye whupped me, Ben," he said slowly. He thrust out a gnarled hand.

As Ben shook the hand solemnly, he said, "Reckon we be friends again now. Pull up ter the table. We're havin' some o' yore pork ribs fer dinner."

****

PITCH

Pitch was cold. It was not the uncomfortable sensation of cold she had known before. She was cold to her very bones; so cold that a numbness gripped her entire body. It made her half drowsy but she was too nervous to sleep.

Sleep just couldn't come to Pitch under such circumstances. She was out of place. Her past life had held no wind-lashed forest trees. Never before had she crouched in the doubtful protection of a rock ledge while round shot-like pellets of wind-driven snow stung her face. Neither had Pitch ever spent a night being serenaded by the ghostly hooting of horned owls.

For the most of her two years of life Pitch had received good care. From the day when she had come to the Lanson home as a coal black kitten to just a short month ago she had known no cares. On that very first day of her arrival she had been received by the two Lanson children with squeals of delight and promptly named Pitch. Uncle Ed had pronounced the kitten "black as pitch" and unwittingly named her.

During the first twenty-three months of her stay at the Lanson home, Pitch had been lovingly, if sometimes roughly mauled by the children. Never had she lacked for food or shelter. If, during the latter months, some of the affection first lavished upon her cooled, it was not an unwelcome cooling. The more sedate taste of an adult cat cared little for childish handling.

In desultory fashion Pitch caught an occasional mouse or rat, and a few times surprised a young bird out of its nest. For the greater part she was an indifferent hunter. Never lacking for

16

food, she found the urge to forage for living things of minor import in her contented life.

A month ago there had come a change. Into the Lanson home had come a fluffy angora kitten. All childish affection and adult tolerance for the nonaristocratic Pitch died. Like the ugly duckling of old she found herself unwanted and to a great degree neglected. In her dumb way Pitch resented the newcomer. So pronounced was her dislike that the family noticed it.

"She hates that kitten," Mrs. Lanson commented, and her husband nodded.

"Natural for her to dislike it," he commented sagely. "Reckon we should get rid of her. We have no business keeping two cats, anyway."

"But who would want her," pondered Mrs. Lanson. "All the folks who keep a cat have one, and besides nearly everyone wants an angora or maltese."

I could easily get rid of her," laughed Mr. Lanson and his wife cried out quickly, "Oh no! You couldn't kill her. After all she's been a pet for two years."

"Wouldn't want to kill her," he answered. "I was thinking of dropping her; just take her out some night and drop her along the road. That's the way people have been getting rid of cats since the days of Noah."

There had been more discussion in the few days that followed. As a result of it all, Pitch found herself that eventful afternoon confined to a box which was closed and dark. There followed a jolting ride over rough road. When the ride stopped Pitch felt herself lifted, and, stricken with terror, she clawed at the inside of her prison. The box lid lifted and Pitch leaped wildly out.

When her first wild flight ended, Pitch was alone in a snow covered forest. A quarter of a mile away she could hear a car bumping over a rough road. Wild-eyed and frightened the cat stared about at the unending forest. At each sound, however slight, she started nervously. When a rotten branch dropped with a crash, she again broke into headlong flight.

What thoughts passed through the brain of Pitch, no one can ever know. As she crouched in the lea of a rock, her body was tense in spite of the numbness of the cold. At every call of the big owls her yellow eyes gleamed in fear, and when a twig

17

snapped under the step of a fox twenty yards away she cowed against the cold rock with her heart beating a wild tatoo against her side.

Toward morning Pitch dozed fitfully. Her body, rolled into a tight ball, quivered even in sleep, and with each awakening she came to her feet tense and frightened. In spite of her nocturnal nature the once sheltered cat feared the dark woodland. It would take time to remove her terror of those swaying trees and mysterious night sounds.

In the cold dawn Pitch ventured stiffly from her slight shelter. She had no notion of where she was going or why. There was no sense of direction in her wandering. She merely moved, following the path of least resistance and winding through the more open parts of the forest.

Movement restored feeling to her numbed body and by the time the winter sun came over the eastern hills Pitch was warmer. She now clung to the patches of sunlight and avoided shady places. Weak though it was, the warmth of the pale sun was welcome.

A small flock of snow birds fluttered from an evergreen. Instantly and instinctively Pitch came to alert attention. Her eyes gleamed and her tail lashed slowly while her body gathered itself as if for a leap. Pitch had never paid much attention to birds before. Neither had she ever been really hungry before. Her quick and tense reaction to the birds was the instinctive answer to hunger.

For several minutes after the birds were gone the cat remained motionless. When she did move there was a purpose in her manner. Her aimless walk was gone. She stalked carefully, eyes agleam and tail slowly swaying. At each movement in bush or tree her body grew tense. Pitch was hunting now. Not the idle pastime urge of a pampered house pet but the intense desire for food drove her on.

Black January woods offer little for a hungry and inexperienced cat. All day, with only short spells for rest, Pitch hunted tirelessly. For a quarter of an hour she patiently stalked a tiny chickadee, only to see it fly away unharmed. Late in the afternoon when the sun had given a tolerable temperature to the snow-covered wood, she waited patiently for an hour on a sunny slope where a wood mouse had disappeared into a rocky

18

crevice. When she finally gave up her vigil, evening shadows were stretching across the woods.

Night brought still cold. Hungry and miserable, Pitch crouched far under the overhanging edge of a huge log. The log was a much more cozy retreat than the bare ledge that had sheltered her the night before. She was warmer but hunger gnawed at her stomach. She slept fitfully but with less fear of the night sounds. On this second night each sound had a different meaning. Somehow it might mean the approach of food.

The second day with thickening skies a portent of more snow, Pitch hunted. Her search became more intent and her eyes gleamed more yellow and bright at each movement. When night came with a thick curtain of falling snow, she crept into her shelter unfed.

With daylight still an hour away Pitch moved into the dark snow-covered woods. Hunger was stronger than fear or the desire for warmth. A sound caused her to freeze. The sound was a gentle patting as though something might be slapping the soft snow. As the cat's gleaming eyes turned in the direction of the noise, a rabbit came into view. He was travelling in slow easy leaps. Each time his feet hit they made a gentle "splat."

Maddened by hunger Pitch leaped too soon. The rabbit sped away in long leaps and the cat pursued with all her speed. Only for a short distance did she follow. As soon as the rabbit went out of sight in a tangle of brush, she stopped. Unlike many other animals Pitch could not follow a trail. Disappointed and angry the black cat lashed her tail and growled, but she had learned something.

That night when she crept into the recess under the log, Pitch remained but a few short hours. Then with the pangs of hunger making her weak she stole out for night hunting. Instinct had come to tell her that cats should search for food in the hours of the darkness.

It was near morning when a sleepy stir and a low twitter came from a low growing evergreen bush. Pitch leaped. Simultaneously teeth and claws closed on the body of a snow bunting.

Even as her body came down to the snow, a growl was welling from the throat of the starving cat. Not once did the growl cease in the scant minute and a half required to tear the tiny bird apart and swallow it. The few drops of warm blood was like wine to the starved animal and even as she licked the last morsel, she growled savagely. Pitch had become a killer.

The tiny body of a snow bunting was only a torment to the hunger maddened cat but it had to suffice. The remainder of the night was spent in fruitless search.

When full daylight came, Pitch found a more protected sleeping place. It was the hollow end of a fallen tree. Dry leaves had been blown or carried into it which formed a perfect bed. With the tiny morsel of the snow bird in her stomach and the warm hollow for a bed, Pitch slept away the day.

That night the cat came out early. Within an hour she leaped upon a wood mouse as it scurried from one hiding place toward another. She devoured it practically entire. Before morning a roosting chickadee was pulled from a bush and eaten. Still hungry and leaner than she had ever been in all her life, Pitch sought her nest in the hollow tree trunk.

The last days of January passed and Pitch still survived. Nightly she prowled the forest in search of food. All too often her search was unrewarded and the hungry cat retired to the tree trunk den with the pangs of hunger unrelieved by so much as a bite. Other nights she was more fortunate. Roosting birds of the winter resident varieties fell most often to her sharp claws. Chickadees, snow buntings and titmice were her commonest prey. Once a scarlet coated cardinal and a big blue jay were caught roosting low the same night. For the first time since she had been in the woods, Pitch felt satisfied as she crept into her bed.

In spite of occasional successful hunts, the cat grew leaner. Her weight was less then half what it had once been. Her fur kept in fairly good condition, but her eyes developed soreness and constantly ran grayish matter. Around the eye the hair came off leaving a ring of bare skin. Pitch was anything but pretty.

During the first week of February, Pitch caught her first rabbit. Dragged to her den, the big cottontail lasted her for two cold stormy days and she did no hunting.

Four nights later death nearly ended the career of the cat. Pitch was stealing softly toward a mound of brushy litter where a wood rat had disappeared. Other eyes had been watching the rat, too. The faintest shadow of something passing between her and the moon caused Pitch to look upward. With split second timing, she leaped, almost too late. The great outspread talons of a horned owl raked her back.

Speeding through the undercover, Pitch carried herself out of danger. She was conscious as she ran of a burning sensation across her back. Two murderous talons had ripped her skin and flesh for a distance of three inches. Cringing in a thicket, she licked the bleeding wounds while growling her hatred of the big pirate of the air.

For the next two nights Pitch remained close to her den nursing her wounds. Then hunger drove her to the hunt again. A wood rat fell to her keen claws and she returned well fed.

February with its deep snows and storms dragged by and March came with heavy rains and spring thaws. Night after night of damp weather Pitch prowled the forest. Wood mice came easier now for with warmer nights they were more active. Flying squirrels, too, on their nocturnal wanderings, were surprised on the ground occasionally. Then with late March the spring birds returned.

Hunting became easier each passing day. The woods were filled with new birds. To make it better yet the new arrivals from the south seemed less cautious. They lacked the alertness of the permanent bird population.

Pitch began to feed well. Seldom did she retire hungry. By the time April brought the first young rabbits out of their nests and the woods resounded to the call of chipmunks fresh from their winter sleep, the cat was a confident hunter.

More and more during the spring days Pitch turned to young rabbits and chipmunks. This necessitated some day hunting but the warm spring air seemed to invite daytime hunts.

(Finished from here by Ernestine Clarkson)

By the time spring had turned to hot summer days, Pitch was no longer a stranger in the wilds of the forest. She had heard the call of the wild and was now a part of that life. No longer did she wander aimlessly around, but with the assurance of a bobcat she hunted her prey. She was never hungry again and no small unprotected animal was safe within distance of Pitch.

It became a game for her to strike every moving creature. This was to be her downfall. Whether she was hungry or not, she killed. Not just to satisfy her hunger but just for the satisfaction of seeing her prey fall under her power.

She was no longer afraid of strange noises, but welcomed

each new sound as another challenge. Her coat became sleek again and her eyes bright. She acquired the speed and slyness of a fox. At times when she felt no hunger she would play "cat and mouse" with her victim.

One hot summer day as she was roaming around she saw an unfamiliar sight. In her usual cat manner she sprang upon the strange creature moving in the grass. While playing the cat and mouse game with the copperhead snake, Pitch felt the sharp pain of its fangs. Little did she know this was the beginning of the end. She jumped back and forth and forgot the pain of the snake bite. Before she finally tired of her new found game, the snake would strike again.

She returned to her home in the hollow tree to die a horrible death. That evening she didn't feel hungry, only tired and sleepy. She slept until morning. She awoke hungry but when she tried to walk she found she was unable to get up. She was swollen and both front legs were completely helpless. Try as she would she was unable to drag herself out of the hollow tree. Finally she gave up and sleep came again to Pitch.

She was awakened later in the day by a loud thunderstorm and rain that lashed against the hollow tree, which was home for Pitch. She pulled herself to the opening to catch the rain on her hot tongue. The cool wet rain felt good on her fevered face. That was the last pleasure Pitch ever felt. Three days later Pitch was gone.

The Lanson family occasionally talked about Pitch and wondered just what had happened to her. Little did they know the hardships she had experienced in her short life after they had abandoned her in the wilds of the dark forest.

****

VENGEANCE IS MINE

A gleam of anger glinted in the usually humorous eyes of Jimmy Kirk, the best camp cook in the employ of the Willow River Lumber Company, as he stood in the doorway of his clean slab kitchen and gazed toward the stables of Camp Five. Out there Sam Hilton was lashing his big team of Percherons into a plunging frenzy. Jimmy shook his grizzled head and turned back to his kitchen.

Dave Hendricks, who was drying his boots by the kitchen stove, raised his head. "Think the Big Boss wouldn't like that, huh?"

"Not by a damn sight," replied the angered Jimmy. "That man ain't fit to touch a good horse. He ought to be run plum off the job."

"Well," laughed the other, "maybe the boss will get wise and fire him. The Devil always gets his dues."

"An' he'll get his," rejoined the old cook. "The hand of God's been on him for nigh onto a year now. He ain't got long on this side o' Hell."

"How's that?" inquired the man at the stove. He was interested now. At his home in a nearby city he had heard of old Jimmy Kirk as a famous storyteller, and he scented one in Jimmy's last remark. When he had arranged at the Milltown company office to stay a week in Camp Five while fishing Willow River, he had secretly hoped to have an opportunity of hearing the famous spinner of tales in action. He felt that he was on the track and pursued it like a hound.

"Do you mean that Hilton is under Almighty disfavor?" asked Dave. "That should be serious."

Jimmy gazed at his companion in genuine astonishment. "Do you mean to tell me you never heard of the Riley murder case?" he asked.

"Never did. But I've been away from this country a lot. Maybe it happened when I was away. I'd like to hear it," he added hopefully.

"Can't tell you now. It's supper time," answered Jimmy. He stepped outside and picking up a hammer began to beat upon a four-foot length of iron rail suspended from a post.

In answer to the clanging summons the loggers came trooping in from outside and took their places at the long board table. Dave joined them and without preliminaries all began to eat as only men who have labored all day in the mountain air can eat. There was little conversation, for the "wood hick" is a man of few words. Eating, with him, is an all-absorbing task.

Dave found himself seated almost directly across the table from the teamster Hilton. Certainly he was not a prepossessing man. Uncombed hair, thick lips and a hooked nose gave him the appearance of an Indian, but his pale blue eyes denied the presence of Indian blood. Dave fancied that there was a furtive and apprehensive gleam in his eyes, but credited the impression to his imagination resulting from Jimmy's remarks.

Supper over, the "hicks" left the room, their caulked shoes digging multitudinous tiny holes in the plank floor. They were a picturesque lot, bronzed and toughened by constant outdoor work among the swaying pines on the steep mountainsides. Each wore the regulation garb of the logger—caulked shoes, trousers snagged off halfway between knee and ankle, checked woolen shirt and hats with notched brims. At first Dave had wondered at the small notches in the hat brims, until someone had explained that each man kept his time by that method. For each day worked a notch was cut. When the circle was completely filled the "hick" went to town and drew his pay. No real logger ever drew his checks until his hat was completely circled.

Dave went out with the others and stood by the door gazing up at the mountains. The last rays of the setting April sun lingered on the mountaintops and deepened the darkness of the lower pine-clad slopes. From Willow River came the eternal song of the water as it dashed along its boulder-strewn bed. Beauty was stamped on every foot of the scene and the man from the city felt that it was good to be there.

A touch on the shoulder brought Dave from his reverie and he turned to find the grizzled old cook beside him. Without comment he beckoned the young man to a bench before the kitchen and the two sat down. Dave lighted the old black pipe that had been his companion on dozens of fishing trips and from his pocket Jimmy pulled a pipe of such proportions as to astonish the beholder. With the blue smoke curling in a cloud about his head, Jimmy began his story.

"Billy Riley was as nice a kid as you'd ever find. Didn't go in for as much cussedness as most hicks, sorta lived to himself while he was in camp. For that reason he wasn't so popular here, but he never minded that. His only trouble was drink. Seemed like everytime he got to town he jest had to start drinkin', but while he was in camp you never seen him touch a drop.

"Billy came in here 'long in the winter over a year ago and went to work. He stuck at the job steady 'til long 'bout the first of May. Then he 'lowed he had filled his hat and was goin'

24

to town. Soon's he drew up, he was goin' on to see his mother down state.

"Down at Milltown the boy fell in with Sam Hilton, the feller I was showin' you today, and after Billy drawed his checks, over three hundred dollars, he left his suitcase with a store clerk and asked him to keep it till he come back from the other side o' town. Said he was goin' to get a drink.

"Well, several people seen him goin' down the street with Sam Hilton and another hick name o' Fenton. Billy never come back for his suitcase and the store clerk started inquirin' 'bout him. Warn't long 'til everyone realized somethin' had happened to Billy Riley, and people got right suspicious o' Hilton and Fenton.

"Old man Riley came from downstate and offered a sizeable reward for anyone findin' Billy. They searched the whole town and dragged the river but not a thing did they find. Looked just like the earth had swallowed that boy. Hilton and Fenton both claimed he'd left them and went on after whiskey.

"Then little bits o' evidence began to leak out. Seems that in Mrs. Flannigan's roomin' house a hick had seen bloodstains on the floor. They was mopped up by next day and Mrs. Flannigan claimed they never had been there. Her house was next door to a nigger house where old Mooneye, as he was called, an' his wife sold whiskey. People suspicioned Billy might ha' gone there to get a drink and then took a room next door and been murdered. Old Mooneye an' his wife acted mighty queer when the cop questioned 'em and things started to look bad for 'em. Then, too, Mrs. Flannigan was awful thick with them niggers.

"Things went on the same for a few weeks without nothin' happenin'. Then one day Mrs. Flannigan and Mooneye's wife got in a quarrel. Nobody knowed how it started, but when Mooneye came up from the poolroom, he found them women, each on their own side of the back fence, a chewin' the rag. Mrs. Flannigan had brought a shotgun out and was threatenin' to kill Mooneye's woman.

"When Mooneye asked what the trouble was all about, Mrs. Flannigan tells him that the nigger woman had vowed she'd tell what she knowed. Mooneye ups and says if she tells a damn word he'll kill her himself. At that his wife turns on him and tells him if he even opens his mouth, she'll send the whole bunch up. That kind o' talk scared Mooneye 'cause quite a

25

crowd had gathered out front and was listenin' to the quarrel, so he grabs the shotgun from Mrs. Flannigan and orders his woman to shut up. She tells him to go to Hell and she'll tell what she wants to tell. At that Mooneye lets go at her and sends the whole load of that shotgun through her neck at close range. She never spoke a word.

"Well, they locked Mooneye and Mrs. Flannigan up, but Mrs. Flannigan would't tell a thing, and when, only three days after the shootin', they had a hearin' for Mooneye, he'd done gone ravin' crazy. Wasn't no sham either. He was plumb gone. But in his ravin' he kept mutterin' 'bout Billy Riley, so folks was certain he knowed all 'bout what happened.

"The cops tried hard to pin somethin' on the others they thought in on it, but couldn't prove a thing, for Billy hadn't been found. They took Mooneye to the asylum and he only lived a month. He died a ravin' maniac, still mutterin' 'bout Billy Riley.

"Right after the killin' of Mooneye's old woman, Mrs. Flannigan seemed to start declinin'. Nobody could say what was the matter with her, but she was fast becomin' a wreck. By the time Mooneye died, she had took to her bed and closed up her roomin' house. 'Bout the time she started gettin' bad Sam Hilton and Fenton left town. They didn't tell anyone where they was goin' either."

Jimmy Kirk stopped and filled his pipe. When it was going again to his satisfaction, he continued.

"Well, sir, that woman just wasted away. 'Fore long it looked sure she'd die, an' no one could say what her trouble was. The cops tried to get her to tell what she knowed, but not 'til jest 'fore she died did they get a thing.

"Seemed Billy had come to her house havin' all the appearance of bein' drunk on doped whiskey. Said he'd got it from Mooneye's woman. She'd put him to bed and later Sam Hilton, Fenton and Mooneye had come over from the nigger's house. They told her they was goin' to rob Billy an' would give her fifty dollars to keep her mouth shut. That was common in her joint so she agreed. Soon after the men had sneaked upstairs, she heard a scuffle an' in a short while heard the three goin' down the back stairs.

"When Mrs. Flannigan went upstairs, she found the room empty and blood all over the floor. Next day Sam paid her fifty

26

dollars and told her never to open her mouth. That was all she knowed. She wasn't even sure he'd been killed and couldn't tell a thing 'bout where to find him. But she did know dirty work had been done an' that fixed her plenty with the Almighty. She died the same night she told that. It sure did start to look like the hand o' God was on them murderers.

"Just after the death o' Mrs. Flannigan, old man Hyer, what lives up the river from town, stumbled onto a body in a laurel thicket. It wasn't much more 'n a skeleton, but the clothes proved it was Billy. Now the body was found, them as was left alive could be tried for the murder. But they was all gone. Nobody knowed where they had skinned out to.

"Finally a detective located Fenton in another state and Hilton was found in the lumber woods of Michigan. How they found 'em I don't know, but there they was at last.

"Well, the trial come on and at the first count they was both found guilty and sentenced to hang. The evidence was plain that them skunks had got Billy doped at Mooneye's house and then come over to Mrs. Flannigan's and killed him. Then they'd hid him in the woods. When Mrs. Flannigan heard 'em goin' down the back stairs, they'd been carryin' the body out.

"Folks thought it was settled, but a schemin' lawyer found a error in the trial and got a new trial for both men. And, damn me, if he didn't get 'em both off. Not guilty was the verdict. They claimed Mrs. Flannigan's confession was no good an' was a result of a disordered mind on account of her sickness. Anyhow there was them two skunks scot free and from all evidence, them the leaders in that murder. Didn't seem right somehow that they should be free and the other three dead, for the others had only been tools. Folks that had claimed divine judgement was ironin' out the affair didn't know what to say. But I didn't say anything. I was still confident that God would straighten out things. An' I wasn't wrong. God's still on the job.

"After the trial Fenton went to the coal mines and got work and this Sam Hilton come here. That was along in the winter and it'd been nine months since Billy'd been murdered. I didn't like the idea o' Hilton bein' here, but I just settled back to wait.

"Now, maybe you don't believe in the hand o' God idea, but all them deaths and all the facts are in the court records of that trial. And here's better proof. That man Fenton hadn't been in the mines over two weeks when there was a fall of slate. There

27

was a dozen other miners near an' not one other was touched but Fenton was killed. That sure looked like judgement and people revived confidence in the Lord.

"I noticed that Hilton looked mighty scared for a few days after Fenton got killed, and the men said he was the most careful man in the woods. But now it's been nigh onto three months since that time and he's gettin' the same as he was. I guess he thinks the Lord has overlooked him, but don't you ever believe it. He's a marked man sure as we set here."

Dave Hendricks remained in Camp Five three more days and during that time had opportunity of questioning many of the loggers concerning Jimmy's strange story. He found that the tale was true in every essential, and found, also, that among those rugged men there existed the same fatal presentment. To a man, they believed the time not far off when the heavy hand of God the Almighty would descend upon Hilton, the sole survivor of the Riley murder case.

The fisherman pondered deeply over all he had heard as he journeyed homeward from the land of the big pines. Somehow a great impression had been made upon his mind.

One week later he sat at a desk in a city office. Through a window the warm May breezes blew in soothing sweetness. Dave picked up his daily paper and the first thing that caught his eye was a headline on the lower half of the front page. "Divine Judgement Overtakes Woodsman." The lead of the short article ran, "Superstitious loggers believe that the hand of God meted vengeance for a year old murder when Sam Hilton, a teamster in the employ of the Willow River Lumber Company at Camp Five, was instantly killed by his runaway team."

"Vengeance is mine. I will repay saith the Lord." Dave Hendricks quoted the words as though unconscious of his speech, and the newspaper dropped to his lap. With a look of awe and reverent wonder his gaze travelled across his desk and out over the endless sea of dirty city roofs. But the gray eyes saw nothing of the city. They were the eyes of a man gazing upon a mighty manifestation, and they saw only a clear retrospective scene cut deep in memory.

Once more the man sat on a rude bench before the slab kitchen of Camp Five. Once more Willow River sang its eternal song and the tall pines moaned softly with the wind. From the stables came the sound of stamping horses and from the bunk

28

house the drone of the loggers' voices. He could see the blue smoke from a giant pipe curling around the grizzled head and kindly face of old Jimmy Kirk, the camp cook, and could hear again his solemn words, "Vengeance is mine. I will repay saith the Lord."

"Maybe you don't believe that, Dave," the old cook said. "There's many as don't. They figger God's on a vacation and don't watch 'em any more. But that teamster out there lashing them horses will believe it some day or my name ain't Jimmy Kirk. One day Sam Hilton will know that the hand of the Lord is upon him."

Dave Hendricks drew himself back from his reverie as though by an effort. The wonder had not left his face, and he gravely nodded as once more he looked at the article in the paper. "Superstitious loggers believe that the hand of God meted vengeance for a year old murder when Sam Hilton, a teamster in the employ of the Willow River Lumber Company at Camp Five, was instantly killed by his runaway team."

Once more as though the words were hammering in his brain, Hendricks repeated, "Vengeance is mine. I will repay saith the Lord."

****

THE WEAKER SEX

It was 8:00 p.m. Jane Black put down the newspaper she had been reading and walked to the window. She glanced up and down the street, and then looked at her watch. She shook her head impatiently.

She returned to the chair in which she had been sitting, and smoothed out a cushion. She sat down with a sigh. And it was then that the doorbell rang three times.

Instantly Jane's entire body came to rigid attention. The muscles of her angular jaw stood out in sharp relief and into her glass colored eyes came a gleam that boded ill for someone. With hands clenched and bony frame erect she hesitated for a brief instant of uncertainty. Then Jane Black went into action. There was no need for haste. She knew the door was bolted and whoever stood without could not enter until she chose to open the bolt.

Behind the big Heatrola hung a heavy iron poker. With soundless steps Jane moved around the Heatrola and removed the poker from its hook. With this formidable weapon in her hand and still with quiet tread she moved through the living room, across the hall, and to the front door.

There had as yet been no repetition of the ringing of the bell, but Jane did not for an instant think the ringer had departed. She placed a firm left hand on the bolt. The poker in her right hand was not raised. She merely held it firmly, pointed toward the floor.

With one quick motion Jane threw back the bolt and swung the door wide. Vacant space met her gaze. Neither caller nor intruder stood in the shaft of light cast from the hall. No sound of departing steps was heard. For ten seconds Jane stared into space. Then for just an instant she seemed to relax, until another thought brought her back to attention. How stupid not to have thought of it sooner. The front doorbell was a ruse. The ringer hoped to draw her there while he hastened to make entry by the back way.

Hastily rebolting the front door, Jane, with quickened yet quiet steps stole to the kitchen. There all was darkness. For perhaps five seconds, she stood in the archway between dining room and kitchen with her hand on the light switch. No sound came to her straining ears. Then she snapped on the light.

Jane could scarcely believe her eyes, for the kitchen was empty. No sign was there of anyone having been there. Jane shook her head in puzzled manner. Perhaps some boy intent on a prank had rung the bell. Perhaps her overwrought nerves had caused her to imagine the sound.

Slowly and thoughtfully the woman turned back to the living room. But the poker was still clutched in her right hand, and her attitude was one of complete preoccupation.

From regarding with vacant stare, a magazine on a stand Jane slowly came again to stiff attentiveness. Her head slowly turned in a listening attitude toward the bedroom that opened off the living room. From that room had come an unmistakable sound; a sound as of some object being moved across the floor. And the realization flashed over Jane that a bedroom window opening on the porch had been left open.

30

Once more Jane Black gripped her weapon more tightly and tiptoed across to the bedroom door. With her hand on the doorknob she hesitated, listening. Then she swung the door wide. The bar of light from the living room showed nothing, but as Jane snapped the switch by the door and flooded the room in light a crouching figure was revealed in a far corner.

Jane Black did not faint; she did not scream or do any of the things women are supposed to do on such occasions. She stood stock still in the doorway, her narrowed eyes regarding the man in the corner with a questioning glance.

The intruder, for his part, seemed to have been thrown for a complete loss. He seemed frozen in the exact position in which he had been when the light was turned on. He had apparently been stooping over near a small cabinet radio that stood against the wall and was now half stooped as though suddenly paralyzed in the act of rising. His face, turned toward Jane, was a scared and pasty one. Frightened watery blue eyes stared at her from behind heavy horn-rimmed glasses and a weak imitation of a chin trembled as though the owner had a violent chill.

Jane moved two majestic steps forward and the cringing figure backed farther into the corner. Jane's hard eyes roved over the room and the intruder followed the focus of her eyes as though hypnotized. When her glance rested on the radio he seemed to shrink within himself and his face expressed the emotion of a cornered guilty pup.

The radio had plainly been moved. One end stood several inches from the wall and beneath that end the carpet had been lifted. A wrinkle showed where the corner had not fitted back to the floor.

A sneering expression crept into Jane's face as she took in these small details and her withering glance froze the man into helplessness. For a long moment she stared hard at him and he withered under her gaze. The poker began to swing like a slow pendulum from her hand and she took a step or two nearer the man still holding him with her eyes.

For a long moment, during which the man in the corner tried in vain to swallow his Adam's apple, Jane stared at her visitor. Then her voice cut the silence like a whip crack.

"Explain," was the only word she uttered, but the man in the corner jumped as though shot. He moistened his lips and made two distinct efforts at speech but speech would not come. He was like an animal devoid of voice; an animal that could register only one emotion, and that terror.

Seeing that speech would not come from him Jane stepped forward and shoved him roughly from the corner. Then she bent over and flipped back the rug. Crisp new money met her glance. She picked up the bills, cooly counted them and turned to the man.

"Where's the balance?" she demanded. And her husband, without a word, handed over his monthly pay envelope from which he had tried to hide three dollars.

****

MOTHER

With sincere soul, devoid of all sham and pretense, I would pay here to the noblest soul I know my weak and ineffectual tribute. Far beyond the power of words is the task to which I set myself. Mouth utterings are not sufficient to voice the innermost feelings of the heart. Only as a feeble whisper may represent and signify the stentorian yet silent inner voice, may I hope to effect my purpose. Only as a bubbling spring may signify an ocean can words tell the heart's adoration.

She is the one person in my life who is weighed in the balance and found perfect. Many times when alone in thought, I have carefully considered her virtues. In my most thoughtful moments, devoid of prejudice or influence of filial love, I have tested and weighed her character. Never so much as a blot or hair weight falls in the debit balance. By every test of perfect womanhood, she is judged perfect.

Truly unselfish is her life and wholly lacking in thought of self. The poor may attest to her bountiful nature that gave without stint from her own meager store. Her family was her first consideration; herself the last. Gladly would she go hungry that her family be fed, gladly dress in rags that they might be warm and comfortable.

Her lot from infancy to the end has not been easy. No bed of roses or flower strewn way has been her portion. Yet she has made the beds of life rosy for others and caused sweet flowers to bloom by the wayside of life for those who surround her. By her own toil has she made other burdens light; by her own silent and uncomplaining suffering has she made the pain of others less deep.

The Christ can be seen in her every feature; her loving smile shows His helping sympathy. Her touch to a fevered brow must surely be akin to the Christ touch. Not by word but by constant example does she portray His constant presence.

And when shall come the time for her earthly parting I know that from her aged body shall go a most saintly spirit. I know that when she enters in at those golden portals the Master himself will come forward to do her honor. And through the saintly throng of that celestial city there shall run a thrilling murmur of glad expectation, and with joy will they say to each other their voices thrilling with music, "She's come, she's come; she who on earth was truly a Mother."

****

NEWS

The long expected second coming of Christ occurred early this morning. The Master appeared at 9:30 at a point two miles outside the city limits. He was first seen there by Will Finley, a farmer who lives on Ten Mile Creek. The farmer offered the Master a ride in his forty-six model Chevrolet but the offer was curtly refused. In haughty manner Christ ordered the man to report to the mayor and state governor that he was waiting there.

As soon as the news reached town, an escort of police and a group of limousines rushed to the place. The governor, secretary of state and head of the state police department made up the hastily formed welcome committee. Police cleared all streets from the point of start to the city hall. No person wearing work clothes was permitted on the sidewalks as the procession passed.

At the city hall Christ immediately made plans to stay at the Ritz Carlton Hotel. The entire third floor was reserved for Him.

At a news conference today He outlined His plans for the future. They are very simple in form and mainly concern a new zoning plan for the city.

All the central part of the place will be reserved for those of pure American white stock who have made at least one million dollars. This region has most of the parks and amusement sections as well as the best streets and utilities.

A second outer circle where facilities are not so good will be held for those of over $50,000 wealth. A few of the better European whites may be allowed to live here.

The working class of people will all be placed in a huge outer ring just inside the city walls. This will be the largest group of all. There will be no electricity or running water here.

All Negroes, Japanese, Chinese and foreign born will be excluded from the city. They will not have either schools, churches or modern conveniences. They will be permitted to work on farms at very low wages.

The editor of this paper joins with the president and governor in welcoming the Master to our land. We feel that everything will be a regular paradise now.

****

THE ETERNAL WANDERER

I saw him on the shore as I fished. He was washing his hands. He was strange yet collected. I can't get him out of my mind. His image has been there so long now that I know I shall carry him always. Perhaps it was that odd intensity about him. Perhaps it was his strange obsession. Or could it have been the piercing haunted look in his dark luminous eyes? Whatever it may have been I only know that I can never rid myself of his memory. He's as real to me fifteen years later as he was that day.

I can still see every detail of his costume: his battered felt hat with the coarse black hair straying from under it; the worn jacket of close fitting dark suede with the row of large white buttons, the close slim legged dungarees of coarse blue denim and the small dress shoes.

That dress could have represented any land. It might have been the costume of a Gypsy minus bright trimmings or it might have been the accidental assortment of charity. No matter what the costume might represent he wore it with an unconscious air of dignity.

34

There was a dignity about his entire bearing. Not the put-on pomp of rich folks, you understand, but a sort of habitual regal manner. He struck me somehow, I just can't fully explain it, like maybe he'd once been a very proud person, rightfully proud that is, and had been forced by some fate to accept a lower station. Somehow, he seemed to bear that station with deep humility; no whining about it nor any resentment.

Of course, likely I'm all wrong about him anyway you take it. It could be he was just a tramp of sorts that had picked up a lot from reading. Or more possible still, he was just a sad mental case; one of those brilliant minds that had gone off-balance. Still there was a rationality about him that I can't quite figure.

I saw him first as I rounded a sharp turn in the river. He was squatting on his heels right at the edge of the water. At first I thought he was humped down there catching bait, but there was no fishing tackle in sight. I couldn't make out just what he was doing and I admit I was curious.

When my feet kicked a rock and made a noise, he straightened up and faced me. He put his hands in his pockets. Not once in my presence did he remove them.

"What luck?" he asked very politely. I was struck by the deep quality of his voice.

"Not very good," I answered. "The trout are just not striking. I've only caught some small ones."

When I finished, he nodded gravely. "There are bad days for the angler as well as fair. It has always been so."

There was not what you'd call friendliness in his voice and manner. Neither was there any sign of hostility. There seemed only one word to describe him and that was "dignity."

I felt like a snoop in his presence for I was trying to see what he must have put in his pockets. I couldn't tell since he kept his hands there, and I couldn't make out any bulges. Somehow he looked guilty, but not the embarrassed kind of guiltiness. It was just more the manner of a man who has faced the fact that all the world knows his guilt and he accepts the stigma of it.

"Fish are scarce now," he said quietly. "At one time these streams were filled with them. Time and increasing numbers of people have diminished their numbers."

"You've been on this stream before?" I questioned.

He nodded. "On its lower reaches. I came here today to test the headwaters. Surely here the water must be unpolluted. It

35

gushes from the very bosom of earth. But," he shrugged in a hopeless sort of manner, "it's the same as all others."

"You a fisherman?" I asked, easing myself down on a stone. He shook his head. "I have no time for fishing."

"You seem to know about fishing." I suggested and again he nodded.

"I see the fishermen in many lands. I am never far from water."

For a time he was silent and I could think of nothing to say. I could only study his face. There was something compelling about it. One moment it would seem to show forth a deep intensity. Then like a cloud over the sun, would come a shadow of something that I could only call sorrow. It was like you'd think you would feel if at one moment you had a great hope and then felt all hopes ebbing away into desolation. Maybe I imagined it, but it seemed the brighter look came when his eyes fell on the foaming blue water of the trout stream.

"The red man before you took countless thousands of fish from here," the stranger offered slowly and thoughtfully. "Throughout this land of America fish were his staple diet."

"I guess that's right," I said. "There must have been plenty here at one time."

"And the coasts," he continued. "There were hoards of fishes. In the days of the Pilgrim fathers what vast schools there were. They dragged them from the ocean in loads to break the nets. Without fish they could not have survived to plant here the belief of the Great Master." His voice broke a little when he said the words, "Great Master" and I thought I had a clue.

"He's a religious fanatic," I thought to myself. "That intense look and those deep sorrowing eyes prove it."

"Fish were a staple of Europe too," my mystery man continued. "In England for example, long before the days of your writer, Izaak Walton, fish were the mainstay of many people. They caught them in traps or made nets that held them. The barbarian hordes of the fourth century were masters in the task of fishing.

"You seem to be an authority—," I began, but he was going on.

"The early Romans, too, were crafty fishermen. Epicures in taste also. They were authorities in the goodness of fishes. They even put fish alive into the hands of guests to assure their fresh-

36

ness. The guest then himself must drop the creature into boiling water."

"I never read that," I mumbled.

"The Emperor Nero liked fishing." A faint look of contempt came over his features and was quickly gone. "But Nero was not a true fisherman. His use of golden nets was more of a show of his wealth. Gold is not good for net making."

For a long moment we both were silent. Then the strange talker went on.

"The deep blue Mediterranean was filled with fish. Its waters were beautiful and appeared pure. The waves were so white, like wool or fleecy clouds."

A look of infinite sadness came over the dark face as he continued, "But those waters were polluted. They could not purify."

"Are you searching for pure water?" I asked.

He might not have heard my question. For a long time he stared through and beyond me. I felt that I was not even included in the general scene.

"Many times," he spoke at last, "I thought of the Lake of Galilee and the rolling River Jordan. They too were not pure."

"The Hebrews were fishermen," he spoke slowly. "The fish was a sacred sign of some meaning to them. I never knew just what it signified."

"Are you familiar with the Hebrews?" I asked.

For just a fleeting instant, there appeared in the sensitive face a faint flash of haughtiness or maybe it was contempt. Before I could be sure, it was gone. His answer was quiet and unemotional.

"The ancient Hebrews, yes. I ruled them."

That proved it. He was a fanatic. I asked my next question to humor him.

"Have you travelled all those lands?" I queried and the strange figure nodded. His next remark really stunned me.

"For the greater part of nineteen hundred years I have travelled. I have gone to the uttermost parts of the world. Always I seek for water. Somewhere, someday, surely I shall find it. Then at long last my soul may find sweet oblivion; the curse of memory will vanish. Surely it is somewhere and surely I must find it—the water that will purify."

His face had taken a dreamy look during the last outburst

37

and I felt that my suspicions were well founded. He was a religious fanatic.

I should have smiled indulgently, but I didn't feel like smiling. My question was timid and sounded strange to my own ears. "Did you say you have been travelling for nineteen hundred years?"

"Not all of it," he replied soberly. "True I have lived many lives. The soul is repeatedly reborn. The body dies but the soul returns over and over again. I have travelled the world throughout all my lives."

"You believe in the theory of reincarnation?" I half asked; half stated.

For a long minute those dark eyes looked at me somberly. I could read nothing in their depths.

"That the soul returns in new bodies is not theory," he stated. "It is fact. To you it has not been shown. You recalled pleasant memories of former life and as a babe you smiled in your cradle. With dawning reason all recollection fled, save perchance a flashing vision not fully identified in later years."

Again he paused. Then he spoke in measured words. "To me is given the curse of memory. With dawning reason, I recall each former existence. I know myself in every change. In each life the cruel whiplash drives me on. My quest has never been answered."

"I don't understand," I said. "What whiplash drives you?"

The answer was very quiet. "You would call it conscience."

With that answer he seemed about to go. In fact he was already turning away. Perhaps he would think it none of my business, but I had to ask one more question.

"What were you doing there at the stream edge when I came upon you?"

His deep black eyes stared long into mine and for the first time I felt afraid. My palms grew wet and my knees trembled.

"Doing?" he repeated hollowly. "What was I doing? Why, what I always do. What I have been doing always since that nineteen hundred years ago. I was washing my hands."

His shoulders slumped and he turned to go. As he moved slowly away he muttered dejectedly, "But the blood is still there."

THE MAGIC NICKEL

He was just a little boy, only half past six, but there was a great empty space in the region of his stomach. He could not remember when the empty space had been so big. Still it was nothing unusual. His mother said over and over that he was never full. Where he put all he ate was just a plain puzzle to her. As for the little boy he never seemed to worry about where it all went.

Tonight Jackie was not empty in the stomach; he was forlornly empty in a social sense. For anyone knows that the loneliest place in all the world is in the midst of a crowd where all are strangers. Around him a gay laughing throng moved but every face was strange.

No, they were not all strange. Sterle was there. But that didn't help. Sterle had recently moved there from his own town but he didn't like Sterle any better in a strange town than he had at home. Sterle was a sissy. Worse yet, he had more money to spend than other boys but he never split any of his purchases. In fact, Sterle's presence made things worse. Sterle had talked to him coolly and then gone off with his stuck-up mother. Jackie's lip curled at the way his fat hips wobbled.

Then, too, Dad was somewhere in the crowd but the crowd seemed so big. When they first arrived that evening, at this enchanted wonderland of a place, Dad had strayed away. Or had Jackie himself strayed? Certainly there was enough to make one stray. Perhaps his body had merely followed his eyes as they feasted on those Elysian booths of good things. For the little boy of half past six was at his first church social.

At such a place no little boy should have been empty or forlornly lonely. To tell the truth this night was the crowning event of a jewel-crowned weekend; a weekend that had promised everthing to make the Arabian Nights insignificant.

When Dad had announced early in the week that on this weekend Jackie was to accompany him to his preaching appointment at an up the river sawmill town, his joy had known no bounds. The remainder of the week had been an agony of slow motion. Each day had dragged even worse than they did just before Christmas.

Then had come the big day; a day so big that a sunburned little urchin of half past six had not even objected to his Sunday clothes. Cheerfully he had donned his usually discarded underwear, white shirt and knickerbocker pants. The black heavy-ribbed stockings and shoes were hot, but he wore them. Even the cap with flat crown, much wider than his head and the snap that held the forward slanted top to the stiff bill, was worn with resigned grace.

Then came the never-to-be-forgotten train ride. There were fifteen miles of enchanted valley with the dashing river always at his side, and with new vistas of delight opening at every turn of the winding track. The raw little sawmill towns along the railway and the staring people on the rough station platforms would always be remembered. Then, too, there had been one station where a store faced the track and there before it had been a pile of watermelons. Those mouth-watering beauties were rare in 1911 and Jackie knew it would be a long time before he would forget the sight of them.

On their arrival today at noon the ever empty little boy and his reverend dad had been gloriously filled at the home of one of Dad's parishioners. Afterwards while the preacher and the family talked, there had been a great two hours of trying out the fine porch swing which adorned the place. Later that evening at another home there had been another meal. Folks usually prepared special for preachers. Certainly the little fellow of half past six could not be starving.

Perhaps Jackie was an exception. Then, again, perhaps all boys have a quality of food consumption that no scientist understands. At any rate, one little boy in the crowd that night felt empty.

And what a place it was to feel empty. Church socials never indicate starvation. The ladies aid for this particular lawn social might have been portraying the Horn of Plenty. There was a booth for ice cream and cake. How it made the mouth water! Ice cream with frosty vapor rising from it was being served in half a dozen colors. From those deep home freezers the ladies in charge heaped it on saucers in piles to make modern day servings look like spilled drops. And with every heaped dish went those tremendous slices of four-layer cakes; cakes in all shades

40

of frosting and inner coloring; cakes that just had to melt in the mouth of anyone who tried them.

Nearby was the pie booth literally buried in pies of all description. Pies with honest open faces stood by their more deceitful cousins whose faces were hidden by rich brown crusts or by fluffy meringue. There were raisin and apple and pumpkin and a half dozen of fruit concoctions. Lemon, chocolate and other new fangled types looked daintily aloof in their white fluff covering. Of course, there were many whose very names no little boy of half past six could call.

More than one booth or table was loaded with homemade candy. Chocolate, caramel and all the fudge family were there. Seafoam in piled platters and peanut studded squares were everywhere. Those booths alone were a little boy's idea of heaven.

Popcorn stands and places where souvenir banners could be bought, got scant attention. There was always popcorn at home for the popping, and who wanted banners anyhow, especially when there was food to be wished for?

Neither did the auction of prepared lunches get attention. Little boys of half past six looked with loathing and contempt on anyone who would pay good money to eat with an old girl. Yet it was true that young men were doing it. Nice looking young men, too; young men with hair parted precisely in the center and wearing the finest of celluloid collars and peg top trousers. Those buttoned shoes were quite elegant too. Nevertheless, there must have been a flaw in their makeup. How else could one explain their bidding on lunches packed by those giggling girls.

Jackie thought them quite homely. His lip curled ever so slightly. He supposed they thought those pinched waists and big puffed shoulders were pretty. Well, little boys of half past six didn't. Just look at all those flashy hair ribbons and the hair itself, all puffed out over their ears in huge bunches. They didn't fool Jackie though. He had an older sister. He knew that inside each of those puffs were three or four "rats." "Rats" were made from all their own saved hair combings, it was true, but the whole hairdo was a fake just the same.

The little boy strayed back to the food booths. There his emptiness seemed more acute than ever. His forlorn feeling grew greater too. It wasn't fair, he reflected. Little boys of half past

41

six ought to have money. Also, at a place like this he ought to see familiar faces.

And there was that snooty Sterle, right at the ice cream booth. He was stuffing himself like a pig. Well, he didn't need any extra stuffing. He was already fat and pink with a soft puffy look. And just look how his fat hips stretched his pants too tight. Sterle looked coldly at the lonely figure and pushed great bites of cake into his mouth. The little boy of half past six turned away. He hated Sterle and all fat boys like him.

Dad had given Jackie no money. Maybe he hadn't thought of it. Maybe, too, he didn't have much. Maybe he just knew everything would work out all right. Methodist preachers with eleven children didn't pass out much spending money. Nickels were very large. Sometimes they looked like wagon wheels. But Jackie had known the thrill of owning nickels. Why once a visiting evangelist had given everyone of the family one.

Little boys who were always empty, needed nickels at a church social as they needed them nowhere else on earth. As Jackie gazed at the ice cream and cake booth he thought about fairies. At his side he heard one woman say to another, "That's the preacher's little boy," but he paid little heed. Thinking of fairies was more interesting. Besides what possible prestige or advantage could come from being the preacher's little boy. With eight more such at home there was little distinction in the matter. But fairies, now, were different. Sometimes they gave people whole heaps of gold and silver.

Fairies usually lived in strange places though. Sometimes it was a strange mountain or in a cave or even in the bottom of big oceans. There just couldn't be any fairies in this crowd of noisy people. Those giggling girls going by with the big combs in their hair couldn't be fairies. Fairies didn't cast those sidelong glances at the swaggering young dandies perched around the pie booth. No, there were no supernatural beings here.

In fact the girls were quite ugly. Fairies were pretty. Take that one who was selling candy. Several young men had been acting silly for her benefit but she was distastefully homely. True, she didn't have her hair in those big puffs. Instead, it hung in long natural curls. Likely it was the envy of the other girls but the boy of half past six knew she'd be very snooty about it. And a young man with a flashy tie and gold stickpin had just told her the tiny freckles on the bridge of her nose were pretty.

42

To Jackie there was just nothing pretty about her. Let her keep her old candy.

Jackie had an idea. Why not look for lost money. Once after a small circus had shown one night near home, he and his brothers had searched over the ground the next day and found three or four pieces of money. He began to search the ground with eager eyes.

Somebody placed a hand on either shoulder and the little boy of half past six looked up. Maybe it was a fairy. No, it couldn't be. Fairies just weren't that large and matronly. Still she smiled with a smile that was kind and very warm. In fact, it was so warm that the forlorn feeling inside was all melted away in an instant. They were only a few feet from the candy booth and Jackie heard her whisper, "Run over there and get you some candy." And into his grubby little hand she slipped something round, flat and hard. He stared at it so hard he didn't notice her departure.

Four strides put the little boy with the empty space near his stomach at the candy counter. How beautiful the girl was all of a sudden. Those curls framed her lovely face and made her look just like the angels in his Bible storybook. And the young man had been right. The tiny freckles were simply beautiful. He must have seen her wrong the first time. Now he just couldn't help smiling at her. Even though she was quite old, all of sixteen or more, she was simply lovely. Across the makeshift boards he pushed the big shining nickel, and pointed to the chocolate fudge. Maybe the young and very, very pretty girl did smile at him just a little special and maybe she filled the paper bag unusually full of fudge. Jackie didn't notice. What he saw was the miracle.

The miracle was, that along with the bag of candy, the lovely girl pushed back the shiny nickel. When he again pushed it toward her, she shook her head with the enchanting smile and Jackie pocketed the nickel.

Even a big bag of fudge doesn't last long when one is half past six and has a large empty space near the stomach. In a few minutes at the ice cream booth a nickel was thrust across the boards and a small voice said, "A nickel's worth of ice cream."

Such a dish of ice cream as came across that counter was never seen before, or since, and all unasked for, along with it came that huge slice of beautiful cake. And again the miracle! The nickel was refused.

The little boy of half past six never noticed that many were looking at him. He did hear the pretty girl, who dished the ice cream, explain to the equally pretty lady, who sliced cake, "It's the preacher's little boy." But such remarks made no impression, even though the girl did smile rather fondly when she said it.

The empty space was not so great when the ice cream booth was left behind, but the pie booth looked very attractive. He didn't know the price of pie but he pushed the nickel toward the waitress and pointed to a big fluffy half of a chocolate pie. Again the pleasing smile, as the half was cut in two pieces and the big fourth put before him. And sure enough the same smile and the nickel refused with again a side whisper to a customer, "He's the preacher's little boy."

Right then and there a little boy of half past six decided that sure enough the matronly lady had been a fairy in disguise, and the nickel she had given him, one of purest magic. Magic it was. It served twice more at the candy booth. Once more it was refused at the place of ice cream and cake. It secured lemon pie equally as well as it had chocolate. It purchased two huge golden bananas.

At ten o'clock the Magic Nickel had just been exercised again at the candy booth when Dad found him.

"Shall we get something to eat?" Dad asked. Strangely the little boy who no longer had an empty feeling answered in the negative.

As the two walked slowly through the moonlight toward Dad's lodging place, they fell in with several others. There was much talk and laughter so no one noticed that the little boy of half past six walked somewhat bent over as though to favor a painful feeling where once there had been an emptiness. Neither did anyone notice that he kept one grubby fist deep in his pocket. There still tightly clutched in a sweaty palm was the wonderful Magic Nickel.

GOD TAKES CARE OF HIS OWN

In his famous sonnet John Milton wrote:
"Thousands at His bidding speed,
And post o'er land and ocean without rest."
I never doubted the truth of that statement. Now since the case of Helena Filuta is settled, I know that the hand of God also thrusts aside the Iron Curtain.

It was an evening in April, the month of April Fools. My wife, Stella, and I both felt like a pair of prize fools. All our fret and hurry of the past twenty-four hours had ended in a thing so trifling.

"All that fuss for a baptismal record which will probably adorn a living room in a peasant cottage where not a soul can read the language on it." Stella sighed as she spoke.

"Yeah," I answered. "But who'd ever believe all the coincidences we met?"

It had all started the afternoon before. We had come into the house to find Dad, a retired Methodist minister of eighty-five, staring sourly at his mail; one letter, no more. Dad didn't like to be treated that way. The only thing he likes better than plenty of mail is more mail.

"Here," he grunted. "You teach languages in school. See if you can make this one out."

He handed me a blue envelope bearing the postmark and stamp of far away Poland. It was addressed in crude printing to *Offis of a Parson, Cass, West Virginia, U.S.A.* The single page enclosed was written in Polish. I couldn't translate a word.

Woman's curiosity for once was matched by man's of equal intensity. We pored over the letter word by word, hoping to find just a few we might recognize. Our search was rewarded only by identifying the name of our own town and the date 1921.

During our dinner that evening the tantalizing envelope lay on the table. Dad had dismissed it from his mind, but Stella nor I could rid ourselves of a feeling of responsibility concerning it. We searched our brains for some acquaintance who might be able to read Polish, but there seemed to be none.

45

Not until nine o'clock did the answer come. Why hadn't we thought of her before? A woman of our acquaintance in a neighboring town had been born and reared in Poland. Feeling a trifle silly for our haste, we threw on our raincoats, for it was pouring rain, and drove eleven miles to the little farming village where the Polish born woman lived.

Bitter disappointment met us there. Our prospective translator was away on a visit. She would not return for a week. Feeling cheated by fate, we retraced our journey.

As we prepared for bed, Stella remarked, "I've been so interested in that darn letter I forgot to lay out my clothes for tomorrow. I'm going to Elkins with Pearl. She's taking her baby over there for a doctor's checkup."

Then the idea struck me. At Elkins fifty-five miles away was Davis and Elkins College. There'd be an instructor there who could translate the letter.

The following morning, while waiting on the doctor's routine check, we idly asked of the office nurse, "Do you suppose the college here has an instructor who understands Polish?" Then the coincidence began.

"Yes, indeed," answered the nurse. "I know her well."

Before the letter was fully explained, the nurse was reaching for the telephone and dialing the college. Within a couple of minutes she was explaining our request into the telephone.

"You're in luck," she said as she hung up the receiver. "The foreign language instructor has an empty period of an hour at this time and was just starting downtown. She says to stay here and she'll stop and see you."

Within half an hour a neat translation lay before us and Madam Jardensky was taking the precaution of addressing an envelope for us in case we replied to the letter.

The translation read, "An Appeal For Help. My parents went from Poland to Cass, West Virginia. I was born there in 1919. Then my family returned to Poland in 1921. My parents are now dead. I need a certificate of baptism. I am sure I would have been baptised, but do not know the church or place. If you can help, it will be so much appreciated. Signed—Helen Filuta."

Into my mind came a vision of many years ago. As a small boy I had stood at the depot when the passenger train came in. As one traveller had alighted from the second car, a swarm of

46

foreign born section workers had rushed forward to kiss his hand. The scene was deeply impressed upon my mind as well as was the explanation given by an older person.

"He's a Catholic priest from Elkins. Comes over here to see members of his church ever so often."

"Where's the Catholic church here in Elkins?" I asked. "If that girl was born in Cass, I bet she was baptized here. There's no Catholic church in Cass."

Strange to say, we were very near the church. In fact it was on the very same street. Immediately we betook ourselves to the church rectory.

There we were informed by the housekeeper that the priest was not at home. However, she could ascertain whether or not the name of Helena Filuta was on the baptismal records.

Sure enough the name was there. Everything was complete with full name, names of both parents and two witnesses. But the housekeeper could not fill out the certificate. A priest must do that.

Expecting to have to call again, we were on the point of departure when there came an interruption. You guessed it. A visiting priest from a Catholic school thirty miles away entered. He could fill out the certificate.

Before we left Elkins, the baptismal certificate encased in the envelope addressed by Madam Jardensky, was in the mail. Along with it went the names and addresses of people we knew who bore the same name, on the off chance they might be related.

Now, back in our own little lumber town, we reviewed the odd chain of "lucky breaks" that had enabled us to fulfill the request for help in less than twenty-four hours after it was received. We learned later of one more coincidence that helped obtain the baptismal certificate. Helena was the only member of her family baptized a Catholic. And at that time no records were kept in the little Protestant church in Cass.

Weeks later from Russia came a letter written in English that read. "I thank you so much for my baptismal certificate. With it I received a passport to visit my family for three months. It had been eleven years since I saw them. No one can imagine how I feel to see my children with my own eyes and feel them with my hands. They are such fine children and well educated by my sister, Antolia. I do not know how to thank my poor sister for

47

my children. She has lived all this time in Russia while I am in Poland."

"My sister, Antolia, is writing this letter. She had finished the eighth grade when we left America and came back to Poland. It has been hard for her to raise my children with only one leg. She is a widow and has only her son to work and keep them and my two sons."

"Now I find that I need a birth certificate if I am to be permanently united with my family. The baptismal certificate isn't enough. Again I ask for help." The letter ended with an outpouring of thanks as did all the letters we received from her through the years.

Again luck, or the hand of God, stepped in. We had kept in touch with a lovely Austrian lady who lived in Cass at that time. A letter from her informed us she had been midwife at Helena's birth. With that, the baptismal record and a search of the 1920 Census, the birth certificate was obtained. In 1961 she was united with her family. We are now convinced that God takes care of his own.

Over the years we corresponded with Helena and Antolia. In them we found a firm faith in God in spite of all their troubles. They were always most grateful for the little things we did for them. Perhaps that is why we believe God takes care of his own.

This story should end here but I was curious about what had happened to this family after leaving this country. So I asked for the story of the life of Helena and her family. The following is just as she wrote it in 1958; and after reading this, I'm sure you will thank God, as I do, that you live in a country like the United States of America:

This is the story of my life after we came from America. When we came from America in 1921 we lived in a small village. We children were very sickly here—change in atmosphere and climate too abrupt. Mother even began to think we would all die. After a year or so we began to get used to the climate. Even mother was a little sick.

After some time, when we were all well again, Mother began to think about what was best to do. There was no school in the village so they began looking for a house in town. They found one and bought it. It was a small town named Berezie, where Antolia lives.

48

Both Father and Mother worked. Father on construction, both bridges and homes. So life went on. We children started going to school. Before the war, we lived not too bad and not too good, not like in America. It's just impossible for working people in Poland to live like working people in America. However, we weren't hungry or cold.

Later we had some help. My brothers, John and Mark, began to work with Father, still in construction. My older brother, Mike, went to America. This I don't remember, if in 1928 or 1929. I remember my older brother some, but very little. Then Antolia got married. And my sister, Olga, and I remained at home. We did housework. In 1936 I got married and in another year, 1937, Olga got married. I am younger than Olga and should not have married until she had wed. So I have had such bad luck. She is living with her husband and children together and I have lost my husband and children.

So we lived in 1939. I can say well and happy. It's the year 1939 that brought such bad luck and tragedy. A year that will never be forgotten, or fully written about either. My husband was called to the Polish Army on the twenty-third of March, the very first mobilization. I was left with one son in my arms and another on the way. My husband has not to this day returned.

Then the war came, August or September, I can't remember the names of the months. It wasn't too bad at first, here where we lived. Bombers flew by to bomb the bridges and such. The worst was, the men that were gone and in the army, and never returned. Soldiers came home now and then. I waited and waited for my husband. At that time I lived on Main Street and would watch from the porch. I could see a long way. I almost "looked" my eyes out. Some soldiers came and went, but not my husband.

I developed such bitterness that others came and mine didn't. And so I lived through the days and weeks. Sometimes I would get so cold, chilled to the bone, out watching for him. Finally my father and brother came and took me back home. The baby was born and I nearly died afterwards. I developed something like blood poison. My family took care of me almost like a child. Some of them were with me every minute, day and night, at the hospital. My father and mother and the rest of the family wanted that I should know I was not alone, was loved and wanted, even if it appeared that I had lost my husband.

49

After about half a year, I began to sort of come to myself. The Lord left me here so that my children would not be total orphans, but would have a mother. But not for long; 1939 brought the Russians. I don't remember what month, but it was terrible. Father and brothers had to go on construction of bridges. The Communists said, "You built for the Poles, you can build for us." Then in the middle of one night Father and my brothers were arrested and spent the whole night with the Russian police. When daylight came they were forced to work. If you were late—prison.

Mother and I waited for them to come to dinner. They came with guards to the door. I was standing at the window cooling food. First we warmed it, then cooled it so it could be eaten quickly. Men had so little time to eat. When they sat down, took a bite or two and promptly went to sleep. They were exhausted. We just could not waken them. They were supposed to go back to work, but just couldn't. They said come what may they just had to rest.

Mother and I begged my brothers to go, drag if necessary. But they and my father slept at home that night. When they were arrested and turned out to work in the morning, they were put under oath under penalty of prison or worse, not to reveal anything that was said or done to them that night. When they left home there were tearful goodbyes for we knew not whether they would return. They spent another night with the police.

The Russians had requisitions to take what was needed and they took whatever their hands and eyes found, even the little food there was, especially shoes. Thus our life was so anxious, uncertain and sorrowful until 1941. The Russians decided to send our whole family to Siberia. In fact, we were ready and at the railroad waiting transportation on Thursday. Then war with the Germans broke out on Sunday, June 22, I think. We returned home and Father and brothers were made to go to work.

The Russians were running, only we did not know it. Later they did not know whether to resist the Russians or to take sides with the Germans. The Germans began infiltrating the town. One evening when Father and brothers were returning from work, they were shot at, either by mistake or on purpose. When the shooting started the men began to run. Father and brother John were killed and my younger brother, Mark, escaped. That was on Monday evening. Next day, Tuesday, my brother and I went somewhere, where the bodies were. When I saw the bodies of my father and brother I fainted. People took me away, and when I came to they brought me home.

My brother claimed the bodies and neighbors and friends brought them home. The older women took over. They dressed the bodies for burial. The men made coffins right quick and we buried them the next day, both in the same grave, without a priest. None could be found.

On Thursday, about the ninth hour a bomb hit our house. Olga's child was burned to death and Antolia was wounded. She lost a leg. The bomb was a fire bomb and everything was burned so quickly. Those that were on the inside were dragged out practically on fire all over. That was a terrible, frightful time. I just can hardly write about it, even after all the years.

The house, barn and everything was burned, and burned so furiously; like all hell broke loose. When Mark dragged Antolia out of the house, his shirt was on fire. Still he went back for the child but could not find it. We never found any remains. We were not the only ones burned out. Our neighbors, too, were burned out and all over town whole families were killed. There was fire, destruction, wounded and dying people. I'd say one half of the town was wiped out.

Mark and I took Antolia to the hospital, and what a hospital! A Jewish school was quickly converted into one. Patients were laid in rows on the floor. There were no nurses and no medicines. Those that had antiseptics, etc., brought them from home and shared them. The Jews really did help a lot, did all they could for the wounded.

Antolia's leg was hanging loose with her whole knee torn out. There was no doctor there in Berezie that could amputate. Olga and I walked to German headquarters and got down on our knees begging for a surgeon. Already a week had gone by and infection had set in. We shed tears and begged and begged on our knees. We begged and even kissed the officer's boots until he finally did send a surgeon. He amputated Antolia's leg and did many other operations—hands, feet, etc. Many died from want of antiseptics and medicines.

We traded and begged with what we had left and got enough medicine to save Antolia's life. It took a lot of perseverance and determination and even a cunning manner to get it. Drugs could only be gotten from the Jews, and, of course, in a war money is

51

no good. So it was trade, if you had anything to trade. Only food was not allowed by the Germans to be traded to the Jews. In fact it was the firing squad for anyone that was caught.

These were terrible, trying times—stay up at the hospital with Antolia at night—work in the fields in the daytime and housework at home between. The children were small. After all the horrible disasters Mother was barely alive. Mark undertook to build a home and I, in order to help out, did man and woman's work too. When Antolia returned from the hospital she began to sew on the machine, using one foot to treadle. I helped her all I could. For the sewing we got food. Like I said before, money was no good for anything.

And so by the hardest we made out to live until 1944. We finished the house and a shed for the cow. Mark got married and we lived altogether. I finally had my own place—small. However, I stayed most of the time with Antolia and mother.

The 1944 year again brought misfortune to us. The Germans ran and the Russians were chasing them. The war at this time was terrible. The Germans left nothing behind them. All cattle and all young people they took with them. They shot, killed or burned the old along with the homes.

We were lucky enough to hide ourselves well, in and around old barns, rubbish, etc. After the Germans left and the Russian soldiers came, we ventured back to town—but what a town. It was total ruins—burnt and destroyed. Only a few buildings on the edge of town were left. My place was burned but Mother's was left. However, it was mined and we had to get Russians to come and take it away.

Life had to go on. We began gathering what was left of grain in the fields and started getting ready for winter.

On the twenty-third of February the Russians arrested brother Mark, and quickly he disappeared without a word or sign. His wife and I hunted, inquired, searched, and not a sign could we find where he was. After the transport with prisoners left for Russia, we searched again for some signs of him, maybe a card or just something to know that he was on the transport. We found a piece of his shirt and written on it in blood, his name and where he was being sent—Siberia.

After two months I was arrested, the twenty-second day of April 1945. One night the Russians came to take me into custody. I fought them off like a wildcat to protect my two small children. The thought of separation and maybe leaving them forever as total orphans nearly drove me insane. No pen can ever write the horrible suffering I went through. A young mother, who had apparently lost her husband, threatened with the loss of her children. When the bombs were dropping from the sky like hail, I held a child in each arm. If we perished, I wanted us to go together so they would not be left as orphans. Now a time came for the worst that could happen. As I said, I fought like a tigress, the two men just could not take me. One went for Antolia and the other stayed to watch me.

When Antolia came I realized it was useless to resist and went quietly. I was sent to prison for years. Even though I did not serve a complete sentence yet I still can not have my children. My heart hurts within me with a longing for them. And when I think of all the suffering, anxiety, uncertainty, horror I went through with, I sometimes wonder how I can be sane.

At first I was taken to an old cellar where there were others that had been taken. Next day, when I heard Mother's voice and the voices of my children, who had brought me food, I tried to tear the door down. I pounded, pulled and pushed, until with complete exhaustion I passed out. It was all in vain. When I came to I was black and blue all over. So the months went by. I prayed earnestly for death, for it would have been easier, but the Lord refused it.

On the sixth day of August or September, 1945 in Berezia, before a Russian military court, I was sentenced to ten years in prison. Ten years! To leave my children, who were my whole life, to be left on the mercy of others besides their parents. On the thirteenth we were taken to Siberia. We arrived on the twentieth of the next month to the place where we were sent. I was very weak after all this torture.

It was terrible there. The people were thin, their clothes ragged and dirty. Before the war I never saw anyone that was so hungry looking, so ragged and dirty. I just couldn't see how I could stand it. I began to think of taking my life. The thought of being absent from my children for ten years, I knew I would never endure it that long.

However, it did not happen that way. They drove us to such hard work, such long hours, six to ten at night, that when I had a minute I dropped to sleep in my tracks. Then the frostbite I got in my legs, the time I spent in the prison hospital, the work again. Living went on, we just can't die when we want to.

I could only write and have a letter from home every six months. When I received a letter my heart nearly burst with joy. So I lived until 1948. I was freed that year by some sort of amnesty. I was brought to Poland. At the Polish border we were received by Polish officers. We were given American packages and some money, 2000 Zlotys. Some had relatives to go to, some had friends, I had no one.

I found a job and went to work. I worked and doctored myself the best I could until the sixteenth of May 1957. I just could not go on. I was ill nine months. I went before something in the government and received 447 Zlotys, just bread and water. That is all I get now. I live the best I can with what I have. I have no family to help me since I am separated from them. I don't mind doing without things if I could just have my family to love.

I don't know if you can read this letter, even if it gets to you. It is splotched with tears. Remembering isn't easy when such a horrible past is brought into view. I have just touched on the horrors. The hours, days, weeks and months, and yes, years spent in horror can never be recorded.

Sincerely,
Helena Filuta

****

THE HOUSE OUT BACK

When memory keeps us company and moves to smiles or tears, we nearly always find ourselves looking backward o'er the years. And there midst our dreams and pictures sits an unimposing house. This house has been sung in song and story so many times that it has become threadbare. I speak of the little red schoolhouse. Now it is not my intention to bore your suffering ears with another tribute to the ancient shack of learning. I do wish, however, to pay tribute to tiny shacks which always accompanied the little citadel of learning. Primly they stood, one on each side, and a country mile back from the seat of learning. They were the originals of all the "his and hers" articles which manufacturers have since exploited. The architecture of those delightful little buildings was simple in the extreme: four bare walls, a swinging door and a perforated bench. No ornaments beyond a few carved initials and a few short rhymes decorated those plain walls. All was unimposing, but to quote James Whitcomb Riley, "In the tragedy of life they played a leading part."

What student of those good old days does not recall the happy hour a day that he whiled away in that ancient two or three holer. There was sanctuary; sanctuary supreme. There the girls found privacy in a realm where no male dared approach. For one shack was the sanctum sanctorum of the fair sex. The other side held equally inviolable territory for boys. And even though the teacher of proper sex might invade those battered walls he or she had no certain way of knowing that any king or queen he might find there enthroned was not there for a serious purpose.

Who of us cannot remember how quickly we mastered that all important technique of holding up one finger as the silent signal for going out. Who of us does not recall how often that same signal was utilized for a stroll in the fresh air, a quiet quarter-hour spent in the solemn quietude broken only by the sleepy buzz of flies.

Yes, it was a grand institution. And while there, our thoughts "on the hole" were lofty and elevating. Many good dreams had their inception there. Many great plans were made, and dreamed through to perfection.

Most students quickly learned the technique of the early "Johnny" system. The one finger signal was mastered in jig time even by the dullest of pupils. The various types of beating in time came more slowly but "on the hole" they were all mastered more rapidly than spelling or grammar.

Take for example the case of Domineck. Domineck was an Italian with little or no mastery of the spoken word. To all queries on the matter of education he had one answer, "me no 'stand." That answer saved him a lot of work and worry that his less fortunate classmates had to meet head on. In a term of school he learned little or no book knowledge but he was less than two weeks in becoming a master of the two holer.

I must admit that at first he was lacking and on one or two occasions he had even utilized an ink bottle with indifferent results. More embarrassing perhaps was his tendency to shout

55

his immediate needs and desires to the teacher. But soon the day came when Domineck held up the conventional finger in the conventional style. When the teacher nodded graciously and he arose from his seat, we knew he had learned the system of "going out." And when he calmly went the long way around the front of the room, stopping by the teacher's desk to select with care three or four crumpled wads of paper from the waste-basket, we knew he went for a serious purpose.

Of course there were occasional tragedies. No system works all the time. For example, there was William. William was very short and very fat with abnormally big ears. He went by the nickname of Jelly.

On this particular day of sadness our teacher was pre-occupied. For long minutes she had pored diligently over some work on her desk. Forgotten seemed the schoolroom. Her eagle eye even missed Mike crawling along the floor to the back seat where the occupant of said back seat slid out onto Mike's back for a cautious joy ride. No wonder she failed to see Jelly's one pudgy finger. Long and with decreasing patience he held it aloft. At first he had held it with quiet dignity, but as time passed dignity decreased and impatience became frantic im-portunity.

When the teacher finally spotted Jelly, he was out of his seat and halfway up the aisle with that one finger waving like a suckling lamb's tail. At her nod Jelly wheeled like a fire horse and hit the door like a tornado. No long imprisoned cat ever hunted dirt with greater alacrity. We heard him thunder down the steps, we traced him, by sound, around the front corner. Then through the side windows he burst into our view. He was going up the winding path with a speed that made his pudgy form seem streamlined. Gravel flew from his digging toes and the path fairly smoked from friction. Jelly was leaning forward straining toward the goal. No olympic runner ever put more heart in his race. His pudgy body lost its pudginess. He was streamlined poetry in action.

No racer had a more attentive audience. Through the win-dows eager eyes followed his flying progress. Necks craned, and against the rules, we stood in the aisles to see better. Our hearts were with him. When it seemed certain he was going to make it our hearts leaped with pride. As Macauly said, "All Rome gave forth a rapturous cry and even the ranks of Tuscany could scarce forbear to cheer."

Then came tragedy. Nearly there and straining to the goal, Jelly stopped. No gradual slowing, no out of breath pause, but sudden dejected stoppage. Had his flying nose encountered a stone wall he could have halted no more quickly. For a long, long moment he stood. Then with heartrending tragedy written in every line of his figure, he turned. A Chinese proverb says one picture tells more than a thousand words. The picture framed by our window told more than twenty thousand words. With the walk and manner of an old old man Jelly made his way back to the classroom. The door that had released a flying projectile opened to admit a woebegone figure; a figure that gazed about the room with misery written deep in every line and angle. Just inside the door he stopped and asked one question that told a world of suffering. "May I go home?" And the teacher being wise, sagely nodded.

****

A RAT'S A RAT

Old Sam was mad. He was, in his own words, "Mad clean through." In fact, as he stated aloud to the four walls of his dirty one-room shack, he had "never been so damn mad in all his life."

A huge rat emerged from a break in the floor and scurried toward the battered old cupboard. That was fuel to the flame. Sam reached for the nearest thing at hand and threw with all his might. The can of evaporated milk struck with a crash that opened a two-inch gash along the top seam. Milk flew in all directions. Sam swore viciously at the hole into which the rat had disappeared. He picked up the milk can and noted that half the contents still remained. For a reckless moment he considered wiping up the spilled milk, but dismissed the idea with a muttered, "Hell with it."

Sam sat down at the littered table. With one sweep of a hairy forearm he pushed aside the remains of his bachelor supper, and glared at the whole assortment of scraps, paper wrappings and dirty dishes. A fly struggling to climb up the inside of a half emptied jam jar caught Sam's angry eye. He slapped a lid on the container, leaving the imprisoned fly to its fate. Muttered curses finding their way through his bearded lips condemned flies, rats and "damned cheats."

From a litter of odds and ends on one side of the table old Sam pulled a dirt grimed sheet of paper and a stubby pencil. His forehead wrinkled in savage thought as he began to write. "Deer surs," was scarcely written when it was marked out with a vindictive stroke of the pencil, accompanied by an audible snarl to the effect that "they's nothin deer about them skunks."

A stiffly formal "Johnson bruthers grosery—cheets" looked better. In fact it seemed so good that Sam immediately addressed a stamped envelope in the same style. He liked the idea immensely. More people might see his complimentary salutation in that way. For a moment he admired the address then returned to the letter.

"If they's anything i Hate, it's a cheet. enyone what Sels a thing an sez its garnteed an it turns out to bee no Dam good is a durty lire an shold bee put outa bizness—."

A sudden burst of squealing underneath the floor brought Sam to his feet. Savagely he stamped his heavy boots on the bare planks and the squealing stopped. He shook his fist at the floor and was on the verge of delivering a profane oration in that direction when a voice from the doorway asked, "Having trouble with your rats?"

Sam started to speak; changed his mind and said nothing. There really isn't much use in talking to a squat, ugly stranger who squints at one over the barrel of a nasty looking pistol.

"Anyone else here?" the gun holder demanded.

Sam found his voice and his own cool nerve at once. "Just me and the rats," he answered.

"How far is this from town?"

Sam pondered only an instant before answering, "Mile and a half when I go in sober. Ten miles when I come back drunk."

"Wise guy," the stranger growled. "Got anything to eat?"

Sam motioned to the table. "A little. Hep yerself."

Distaste showed on every line of the caller's face as he inspected the remains of the supper. "Not fit for a hog," he remarked. "But I have to eat."

"I live on it," Sam answered, "an' the rats git fat. You kin make out onct."

Still keeping a wary eye on Sam and with the gun ready the stranger picked a slice of bread from its wrapper and folded it around the two slices of cold bacon left on the plate. With his mouth full of the first bite he pointed with the pistol to an egg lying on the table.

"Fry that," he ordered.

"Caint," Sam answered. "It's aready hard biled."

Tapping over it with the gun barrel the man crazed the egg shell and began to peel it away. Sam watched with little apparent concern. When the egg was peeled he spoke.

"Reckon you be the feller what killed an robbed the payroll carrier at the sawmill yestiddy."

The other nodded and Sam went on. "Swanson, I bleeve they called ye. Cops musta been wrong. They think ye skinned outa the county."

"That's what I want them to believe," Swanson answered. "Too many people know me. I'll have to travel by night. Before morning I will be out of the county." He finished the egg and sandwich and began to rummage among the dishes, cans and paper bags.

"Some jam there," Sam suggested. "Goes purty good on bread."

Swanson rejected the jam with a shake of his head and peered into a brown paper bag. From it he drew a handful of small cracker like biscuits. As he munched a mouthful of these, he picked up the half empty milk can.

"Got some water?" he asked. Sam pointed to the bucket on its stand by the door.

Into a glass the robber poured the remains of the milk and finished filling the glass with water from the bucket.

"This stuff's too rich to drink straight," he stated, and Sam nodded agreement.

Back at the table Swanson sipped milk and ate biscuits from the bag. Sam watched with greater interest but said nothing.

When the glass was empty, Swanson pushed back his chair and tapping the table top with the pistol for emphasis he stated, "Now I'm leaving. I suggest you stay right here. If you should try to hike into town and tell the cops about me, I just might be waiting along the way and you just might get shot."

Sam nodded in perfect agreement. "That's jest fine," he said. "Be a waste of time enyhow."

Swanson backed out and pulled the door shut behind him. Sam didn't so much as go to the door or window to look out. He smoked a pipe, undressed partly, blew out his smoky lamp and went to bed.

At six o'clock in the morning Sam stretched, yawned and squinted at his old alarm clock. Then he turned over for another hour of sleep. At seven he got up, dressed and went out to get a load of wood.

Fifty yards beyond the woodpile something lying in the pathway caught Sam's eye. He walked over to it and gazed down at the very dead body of his caller of the night before.

Sam turned back to his shack, stopping on the way to get his armload of wood. Inside he picked up his coat and hat.

"Have to go to town an tell the cops he's here," he said to himself. Then as his eye swept the table he added, "Jest as well mail my letter while I'm a goin'."

Slowly Sam read what he had written the night before. Then in his laborious scrawl he added, "never mind what I writ above. Yer pizen biskits duz kill rats afore they kin travel a hunerd yards."

Yours respeckfuly,
Sam Adler.

—Used by permission of the *Charleston Gazette*

****

THE POSSUM AIR A REBEL

The possum air a rebel shore as shootin. Pears like you caint read nothin about them states down south thout a dang possum stickin his peaked nose into the pitcher sooner or later. He's purty nigh as much a part o' the country es a mule or the democrat party.

Now hyar in West Virginia we aint rebels and we aint yankees, seems as how we kinda sot on the fence endurin the scrape atween the states and fur ez both sides air concurned we still air a settin thar. One third o' the peeple thinks we belongs with the south, and one third thinks we lean north and tother bunch don't know they is no sech a place to begin with.

Mebbe all this air why we air kinda hot and cold on the
60

possum. Most folks around here caint git up no mouth waterin action atall when enyone talks about roast possum and sweet taters. Down south I hear as how they claims its a dish fit fer a god but up north the yanks claims it aint fit fer a god spelt backwards.

Jest as we wuz kinda mixed up in the big scrap of the sixties and fit a lot again each other, so we air also mixed up on the possum. Some folks sez he's good, and others sez they wouldn't eat him if they wuz starvin.

Well, sir, like a true West Virginian I'd bin a fence setter fer a long time. That is, I hadn't et one o' the critters yet but wuz thinkin mebbe I'd try him some day. Then fate er accident er sumthin stepped in to settle the matter.

Tex stopped at my gate one day an hollered in that we wuz goin possum an coon huntin thet night. Seemed he hed a new houn thet wuz tops in such huntin an he wanted to show him off.

I shoulda knowed bettern to bite on one o' his trips. Lord knows I'd done got in trubble enuff a foolin around with him. Seemed like ever time I went out with Tex, things turned out all rong. A follerin after him I'd been stung by hornets, chased by bulls, shot at by farmers and a dozen other bad things. The old woman allus lowed as how I hed to take one more trip with him cause I hedn't ben bit by no rattlesnake yit.

Enyhow me an Tex an the houn dog started out thet night jest about the time the big hoot owls wuz gittin tuned up. It wuz a purty moon shiney night and didn't look es if anything could heppen cept good luck.

"We'll ketch plenty tonight," Tex sez.

"Yeah, plenty o' hell," I answers.

"There you go gripin aready," says Tex. "You'd gripe in paradise if—"

Don't know what Tex wuz goin to say cause jest then the houn started bellerin. He hed a voice like old man Miller's hereford bull.

"He's a headin up Glory holler," Tex sez. "Thet's the way we wuz goin. Ain't thet luck?"

"Shore is," I says. "If he gits near the pig ranch old Susie will shoot him."

Old Susie lived in a shack whut we called the pig ranch cause her old man usta steal pigs. Her old man wuz dead now but

61

Susie could swing a mean shotgun an she didn't like noise round her at night.

Well, sir, thet houn tuk as strate fer the pig ranch ez you could shoot a arrow and fore we could git half way up the holler, he wuz barkin treed some place near old Susie's shack.

Fore we got to the clearin we could hear the racket. Our houn wuz barkin like he had rabbys and old Susie wuz a cussin in the shack so loud we could hear her from the edge of her corn patch.

When we run to the pig ranch yard we seen our houn on the back porch a jumpin at the door, an there perched atop the screen wuz old Susie's tom cat. Me an Tex both yelled at that fool houn but he paid us no mind.

"We gotta git him," yells Tex as he starts in the yard gate. I staid outside expectin him to git shot any minute.

Bout the time Tex got his hands on the houns collar, the back door flew open and old Susie come out with a broom a flyin. Tex backed outa the yard draggin the houn an Susie stood on the porch and cussed us all.

"If I'd a had a shell fer the gun, I'd a killed thet dawg," she yells.

"I'm glad she didn't have a shell," Tex sez as we leg it away from there.

"I'm glad she didn't have three shells." I pants as I try to keep up with Tex.

After a while we got about a mile er so on up Glory holler and old Susie's cussin started to die out in the distance. Tex lets loosen the houn and figgers mebbe he won't go back after thet cat. We don't stir up nothin more in Glory, so we tuk acrost a rige and drapped down into Slick Run holler.

Slick Run is a purty good sized little crick and has a cupple old splash dams on it. They wuz used to dam up water fer flotin logs out back in my daddys time. Most o the dam work wuz rottin now but at one o them we figgered we could cross the crick on what wuz left. We got about half acrost on the old slick log spillway when they wuz the dangdest splash ye ever heerd. The splash wuz me hittin the water jist below. Mebbe that's how they come to be called splash dams. Enyhow I swum out and hed sense enuff to head fer the bank where we wanted to go.

Tex he laffed at me real big till I offered to hit him side the head with a rock if he diddent shut up. I wuz wet enuff an mad enuff to fight a wildcat.

Just on tother side o thet splash dam the houn started to beller again. "I wonder whose cat hez been hyar," I asked sarcastic like and Tex gits a little peeved. He don't like no one makin cracks about his houn.

After a short run the houn barked holed and we found him near the crick diggin like he had a bone burried in thet bank. We'd brung a mattick an so I startcd to diggin hard. It warnt thet I wuz so ambishus, it wuz cause the work kep me from freezin to death.

After bout a hour o diggin we got fur enuff back into the bank to see what we wuz after. It wuz a big possum. I could see his long rat tail. Most possums is sleepy critters so I jist grabbed that tail and give a yank. That dang possum swapped ends so quick his head end caught his hind end goin and fore I knowed what it wuz all about, he hed two o my fingers in his mouth. I wuz sure I felt the bones crack. I never hed nuthin bite me so hard. It felt like them fingers wuz in a vise with a team o horses hooked to the turn screw. When I got the rat eyed critter loose, most o' the meat wuz gone offen the fingers.

Tex pinned the critter down with the mattick and kicked the houn outta the way.

"We want him alive," Tex sez. "We gotta fatten him a little fore we eat him."

"Fore we what?" I sez.

"Eat him," sez Tex. "Roasted with sweet taters he's the best grub you ever tasted."

"How many you et?" I asks while I'm tyin up my fingers with a hankercheef.

"Ain't et none yit but I'm a startin on thisn," sez Tex. "I read in a magazine bout how to fix em. We feed him on cornbread fer bout a week then we'll hev one larrupin feest."

Tex appointed me to carry thet varmint. He allus wuz the execketive tipe. Claimed the mattick and houn wuz all he could handle.

"Jist pack him by the tail," Tex sez. "If he tries to climb up hisself to bite you, jist shake him. Purty soon he'll carry peaceful like."

Well thet blamed over growed rat never did try to climb up hisself to reach my hand. He jist spent all his time watchin to

63

grab my leg if it got clost enuff. An the way Tex waved the lantern round and led me into clost places looked like he wuz a helpin the possum all he could.

All the way Tex wuz a talkin bout how good thet roast possum wuz gonna be with them golden brown sweet taters round it.

"It's bettern chicken," he sez. "Down South no one would look at a chicken if they wuz possum on the table. Even bettern pheasant breast accordin to some. Yes sir, we got a real feest here."

Bout thet time the "feest" bit me a good one on the calf of my leg and I hed a hard time not hittin Tex acrost the head with him. Some way ever time I looked down at thet grinning rat, I lost a little more o my desire to eat any o' him. But Tex wuz still ravin on.

"Might invite some company," he sez. "Be a shame not to let some other folks in on this feed."

"Mebbe you can invite someone in my place," I suggests kinda hopeful like.

But Tex he sez, "No sir, you helped ketch him and you git to help eat him." Thet's another thing about Tex. He keeps you at it till the trubbles all done.

We come home by Brogan's farm. Tex sed it wuz a near cut. First time I ever seen a near cut thet wuz longern a fur cut. On the way thet possum bit me or snapped my pants leg no lessen twenty times.

Jist as we come round old man' Brogan's pasture, we ketched a awful smell in the air. Somethin sure wuz good an dead round there and clost too. The houn he noticed too and sniffin kinda eager like he turned into a little dip.

When we went down there, we found the dog a sniffin round the rotten carcass of a dead horse.

"I heerd thet one o' old Brogan's horses died a cupple weeks ago," sez Tex. "Guess this is his remains."

"His remains sure stinks," I sez. "Let's git outta here. If thet houn o yourn eats any o thet horse, he'll stink till jedgement day."

"He aint gonna eat it," Tex tells me. "He's jest tryin to figger it out."

Sure enuff the houn wasn't tryin to eat none o thet horse. He jest kep sniffin at a place where a hole hed caved in on one o the horses sides. Then he started to whine, an at last he give a cupple excited barks.

"I wonder," sez Tex and he pokes a stick inside thet horse. He stirred up a lot of fresh stink an then outa thet hole comes a big fat possum. The houn grabs him and shakes him good nough to either kill him or make him play dead.

Tex begins to look kinda funny an I begin to geel like somethin wuz crawlin on my insides. Tex holds the lantern up an we both peep into thet hole in the dead horse. Inside crouches another possum and all across you can see where they been eatin on the inside o thet rotten horse.

"Let's go," sez Tex. "Don't like the smell o this place."

"Wait a minute," I sez.

Tex didn't say a word when I set down thet varmint I wuz carryin and kicked him into the next county.

"I'll hev my sweet taters straight," I sez. "Don't believe I'd keer fer no rebel cookin nohow."—Used by permission of the *Charleston Gazette*

****

BABIES

As an eminent authority of no experience I have come to elucidate you on a crying subject. I expect to expostulate on babies. Now you young jerks on the back seats—I saw you straighten up and look silly—just settle down—I'm not talking about the kind of babies you're thinking about. I'm talking about the real thing.

Now to begin the mighty interrogation. Where do babies come from? Well, there are several theories—some say doctors bring them in little black satchels. Personally I don't believe that one. Why don't I? Well, those little old satchels are too small to hold twins and even if it is twins you never see old Doc carrying but one satchel. Another thing—if docs brought them, you could order whatever you want—that is a male or a female. But you don't, you just take what you get and ask no questions. Furthermore, if docs brought them you should be able to get a choice. They'd have a few samples on display and you could pick out at least the pattern and style you liked best. But do

65

you get to make a pick? You don't. At least if you do some of the little mutts I've seen must have been picked in the dark.

Another thing—if doctors brought them in this day of competition, they'd be making some kind of guarantee of satisfaction or else take the defective product back. But who ever heard of a doctor taking one back?

I know you'll argue that Doc's nearly always there at the time, but that doesn't prove a thing. He merely gets there first to get first pick on the cigars.

Then there's the theory that angels bring them. Maybe so—maybe so. But I don't believe it. Why at the rate they're appearing now it would take all the angels in the United States and Georgia to bring them in. Besides that the angels have too much other work to do. Just think—hang out the stars—take in the sun—light up the moon—then come morning and take in the stars—put out the moon and roll out the sun. And in between times push clouds around all day. They just don't have time to bring babies.

I have heard the belief that babies come from busted cabbage heads. I don't believe that either—in spite of the fact that lots of them turn into cabbage heads later in life. No sir, that idea is just plain silly. Tell you why. Some come in winter when they ain't no cabbage. Guess that proves that.

All in all we'll just have to admit that where babies come from is a mystery.

Now there's all kinds of babies. They's dry babies and wet babies. They's black babies and white babies. They's girls and boys. They's baby pigs and baby ducks and baby fish and even baby elephants. Once a guy showed me a fat lady and said, "There goes a baby elephant." I took after her and walked around her three times or four. When she asked what I wanted, I said, "I'd like to see your trunk, that guy said you was a baby elephant." I was in the horsepital four months.

Funny thing about babies—take baby pigs. They come in family lots. That's mass production. I knowed a family that got one new one every single year; they called that assembly line production. One family got twins once—claimed they'd been on the double or nothing program.

Now I wish to discuss what to do before the baby comes. It's really simple. You buy ten flannel undershirts and twelve dozen safety pins—fifty squares of cloth, twenty-four by twenty-four and one gross of safety pins—five blankets and a few packs of safety pins. Some people who likes to show off gets a teething ring, but you don't need that—any kid that can't cut his teeth on a table leg or an old boot heel ain't worth his salt.

Along with other things you better get a bottle of castor oil, an old wash tub and a few boxes of cigars. At the time of arrival one thing is very important—take the father out and tie him to a tree. Otherwise he'll wear out his shoes pacing the floor. On second thought, take his shoes away from him and let him wear out his feet.

When the baby comes he's supposed to cry. If he don't cry, pull his tail and see if he'll bark. I knowed a feller back in 1918 that had some monkey glands installed by some big doctor. Said it would make him young again. Well sir, when his next baby come, it took two hours to get him down off the chandelier so they could tell if it was a boy or a girl. They finally coaxed him down with a fresh cocoanut.

Babies have some things right at the start, such as good lungs, bald head and a red complexion. They don't have such things as hair, teeth, or vocabulary.

Some babies look like their mothers but some unlucky ones look like their old man. Good little babies are just like mom, but every time one gets meaner than a water snake mom says, "He's getting more like pop every day he lives." Babies get measles, chicken pox and colic. When they get colic, the best cure is to roll him on a barrel face down. If you don't have no barrel, lay him over your shoulder and jump up and down for two hours.

Babies also has tantrums—but tantrums ain't caused by germs. Tantrums is caused by babies gettin' to be like their parents. Most tantrums is taken after babies is two or three years old. Don't be alarmed now—tantrums can be cured. A folded magazine, paddle or pancake turner applied briskly to the anatomy usually cures tantrums. They also serve as a sort of vaccination against return of the same symptoms.

Course you will not be very successful with the little brat but don't worry too much. Just suffer along with him for six years then you can turn him over to some poor schoolteacher and give her the blame for ruining your little angel.

****

THE GOOD OLD DAYS

In the days of old when nights were cold
The snow came through the ceiling.
While we roasted our faces at old fireplaces
Our backs were too frozen for feeling.
The day we were born we began to drink corn
And eat wheat cakes by the stacks.
We wore skin togs; lived in houses of logs
Where the dogs came in through the cracks.
The boss of the clan, a mighty old man,
Was Grand dad, aged ninety-seven.
He walloped our tails with hickory flails
To give us a start toward Heaven.
We learned to shoot or we got his boot
In a place I won't here mention.
And a center shot or a "cut the spot"
Was the only kind worth attention.
Every two years we washed our ears
And sometimes even went swimmin'.
We chewed "home spun" and fought for fun
While the work was done by the women.
The "Johnny" shack was a way "out back"
And the holes were cut on the square,
The trip was tough and the cobs were rough
And we didn't tarry long there.
Oh, the days of old; Oh, the nights so cold
That time has put to rout.
They've not been here for many a year
But they sure are lied about.

Recently a group of store-porch philosophers were discussing the weather (rather odd subject to be talking about). A twenty-four-year-old Plato remarked that the winters of the present time are not as bad as they used to be. "Why, twenty years ago," he declared, "the snow would often be up to my waist." Another philosopher looked his long length over critically

68

and remarked, "Twenty years ago your waist was a dang sight closer to the ground."

That remark started my single cell brain to work. That unusual exercise brought about a nasty little suspicion. Could it be possible that some of those tales we hear about the good old days were a wee mite enlarged?

Now don't get me wrong. I'm not making any flat statements. I'm merely suggesting. Maybe old Simon Pettijohn did get twenty-seven coons and eighty pounds of wild honey out of one hollow tree. Far be it from me to dispute his solemn word. Come to think of it, that tale must have been true for he told it not fewer than a thousand times and the number of coons never varied more than eight or ten.

I wouldn't openly say that Silas Horne didn't kill forty-three deer one week using a muzzle loading rifle. The only thing I question was that part about running out of bullets and killing the last thirteen with hand hammered horseshoe nails.

Before I go on, let me say that I do firmly believe that the snow was so deep during the winter of '83 that a horse broke through the crust and was found next spring in the crotch of a tree forty feet from the ground. The reason I believe that one is that I have seen the tree, not fewer than a dozen times in as many different places. You just can't doubt evidence like that.

But I like to hear about the "good old days." Such winters as they had! In November the snow fell to a depth of eight feet and the ground was seen no more until late March. The rivers froze solid and were used as highways. Ice four feet thick was only standard. And during that time, as near as I can gather, the thermometer never rose above twenty below zero.

Of course we couldn't leave the subject of weather without mention of those time-honored educational difficulties. Remember how Dad burrowed through those five long miles of mountainous snowdrifts to reach the little one room school? Remember how he fought subzero blizzards, determined to be educated or freeze to death? Wouldn't you have enjoyed dinner with him as he thawed his frozen cornbread and apple butter on the pot bellied stove?

And what an education he got! We had teachers in "them good old days." Dad could quote every rule in Harvey's grammar and could spell every word in the dictionary. He worked like a galley slave. None of this soft modern day schooling for him. He went to school to get an education!

How Dad ever found time to whip the teacher once a week, stop up the schoolhouse chimney, put blasting powder in the stove and dump over the toilets every Halloween is a mystery to me. But Dad says he did, so I suppose he did.

I would like to have seen some of the men of "the good old days." They must have been monsters. I like to hear about Uncle Andy who never stooped to drink cider. He just picked up the barrel and drank from the bung hole. He's the gent who fed his horse ten ears of corn then sat down to his own table and polished off twenty-two roasting ears. It was his brother who plowed fourteen acres in one day then walked twenty miles to the store to get a fresh plug of tobacco.

I used to question the tale I hear about the old Fourth of July mule race. It seems that Uncle Andy's mule broke a leg in the first lap but that didn't worry him. He just finished the race carrying his mule. I don't question that story any longer for in recent years I saw the very track where the race was run.

None of those old-timers were less than six-foot eight in height and very few weighed less than 220. Some could only be weighed when they chanced to be at the local cattle scales. Their size was only matched by their tremendous deeds. What a lot of sissies their grandchildren have turned out to be. Among those old boys a runt like Joe Louis would have lasted about as long as the proverbial snowball in hell.

The crowning glory of the old days was the game and fish resources. Those days were a hunter's paradise and a fisherman's dream come true. Fifty deer for a winter's kill wasn't even worth mentioning. And what deer they were! Three hundred pounders were classed as fawns. Most old-time horses were swaybacked from carrying in those monsters. The horn spreads were fairly well standardized. They were just as wide as the ancient hunter could reach with both arms extended.

They had some good bears too. Take, for example, the one Pete Lanley choked to death over on top of Gandy Mountain. It tipped the scales at just 951 pounds. If it had been fat it would have been a real one. As it was Pete only rendered out 33 gallons of bear oil and he used practically all the surplus fat. First time I heard about that bear, his hide covered the entire living room floor. Last time I heard it mentioned they were using the same hide for a circus tent.

One old-timer told me of going on a rabbit hunt in a two-horse wagon. I mentioned that such practice sounded lazy. Then the old gent reminded me that the wagon was used to haul home the rabbits.

Most real hunters of "the good old days" didn't bother with hunting turkeys. When the family desired a turkey dinner the girls went out and got a couple with beanshooters.

Yes, wildlife was plentiful then and even the amateur fared well. But there was an unpleasant side too. For example, according to what I hear, you could scarcely ever raise a sheep or pig. The wolves and wildcats ate them all. Also when one went to bed in the breezy family attic he invariably awakened to find himself in bed with a sociable panther.

When Grandpop went fishing the women of the whole neighborhood gathered to help clean and salt the catch. And were they the big ones! What we have mounted now Grandpop used for bait. Practically every "old days" trout fisherman had a deep notch worn in his arm at the 27-inch mark from showing his friends the approximate length of the good ones.

All considered, it must have been great to live in "the good old days." Now during our easy winters we pygmies sit in our comfortable homes and dream of going back to the days of old. The dream is always pleasant up to a certain point. That point is reached, for me, when I realize that had I lived in the days gone by, I would now be as dead as Julius Caesar.

****

BRINGING HOME THE DOG

"Yer see boys, it's this way; all o' the top o' Cheat Mountain is jest a little patch o' Canady that run away from home. It's a furriner o' sorts. Jest don't belong down hyar in West Virginny atall."

Scotia Mike raised the ponderous weight of a caulk studded Cutter shoe and, with both hands giving an assist at a rheumatic knee, crossed his legs. That done he applied a match to a huge

71

briar pipe while squinting one eye in our direction. Hollows appeared in his stubby cheeks as he puffed huge clouds of smoke.

"Yessir," the old logger continued, "Cheat is land out o' place. Yer don't hafta believe me. The book fellers'll back me up. That patch o' land is Canady gone astray. Why if I was to a gone ter sleep in Canady, where I usta work, and hed woke up on Cheat I'd never a knowed I'd been moved."

Remus and I, Scotia Mike's listeners, knew for a fact that the old woodsman had come into our section of country from Canada. His nickname Scotia Mike was a shortened form of Nova Scotia Mike. We had that much foundation upon which to build acceptance of his stories. Let it be said that some of Mike's stories needed plenty of foundation.

"As fer them rabbits yer ask about; sure they're up there. Snow white in winter and brown in summer they are. Mind yer now—they got no business this fur south, but I ain't one to argy with facts. They's scads o' jack rabbits up there. Though I'll tell yer they ain't rightly jack rabbits. They calls 'em snowshoe rabbits up north and that's the right name fer 'em."

"How big are they?" I asked. For several of my sixteen years I had been regaled with logger stories of those mythical white rabbits that supposedly inhabited the high top of Cheat Mountain. In size the rabbits ran from "a couple times bigger than a cottontail" to "about the size of a medium sheep." Why someone from town had never gone out to prove those rabbits I don't know. Perhaps there just weren't so many hunters then. And, too, Cheat Mountain was a forbiddingly cold place.

"How big?" Mike pondered. "Well, I'd say jest a little less than Sambo there," and Mike indicated, by spitting toward him, the town barber's medium-sized bulldog that sprawled on the splintered boardwalk in front of us.

Remus and I exchanged glances. Sambo would have weighed all of thirty pounds. Even sixteen-year-olds who had never seen one of the famous white rabbits knew better than to swallow that story.

"Course now," Mike qualified, "they might not weigh as much as Sambo. They're built kind o' ganglin'."

"Where could we find some of them?" we asked.

Mike absent-mindedly scratched his ribs through the rough wool of his red checked Richie shirt. "Damn graybacks is

72

hungry today," he muttered. "Camp Nineteen is the best louse hatchery on Cheat. Don't ever spend a night there, boys. You'll be et alive. They's graybacks in them camp beds as will eat all the meat off one side o' yer and wait hours fer yer to turn over an give 'em fresh chawin space."

"Aren't all the log camps as bad for lice?" I asked.

"Seven ain't as bad," Mike answered. "It's worse. Sixteen is a little different. Not near so many but lots bigger. Why, they's graybacks in that camp bigger'n June bugs. The boys use 'em fer trout bait when they fish Cheat River."

His scratching finished, Mike returned to rabbits. "Now lemme see. Where could yer find some snowshoes? Why that's easy. You boys jest hop on the log train some mornin' and ride to the top o' the mountain. Right after yer top up, roll off and take any cove to yer right. That'll be old Camp Five territory. Snowshoes is thick in that cutover land. In a day's time with a good dog you'll kill more'n yer both kin carry."

"Maybe we could borrow Andy's hound," I pondered.

"Big Jim's got a new rabbit hound," Remus interrupted. "He says he paid twenty dollars for him and he's guaranteed to run rabbits. Just yesterday Jim told me I could take him out some day and try him. He wants him exercised."

"Them snowshoes'll exercise him," said Mike. "They kin cover twenty feet at a jump an' they run a two-mile circle."

"We'll have to be careful if we borrow Big Jim's dog," I said. "He sure would raise cain with us if anything happened to his hound." In spite of the fact that I was now old enough to be out of the town's three-room school, I couldn't repress a tremor at mention of Big Jim. As local truant officer and district constable he was the terror of all hooky players.

"Nothing will happen," Remus answered.

Early the next morning two heavily clad boys climbed aboard one of a long string of flatcars which stood on a siding at the big sawmill of the West Virginia Pulp and Paper Company. Number Eight, the huge cog driven Shay engine that made the daily haul to and from the top of Cheat Mountain was panting impatiently at the head of the line. Brakemen were making last minute preparations for the start. Between other tasks they offered to Remus and me plenty of advice on how to handle Big Jim's hound.

It appeared now that, whatever other training the new dog

may have had, riding the flatcars was not a part of his education. Twice we got him on and twice he jumped off. Each time required a chase to catch him. The third time aboard was the charm. That time we twisted a length of wire around his collar and tied him to a pile of boom chains.

During the process of loading the hound a new problem presented itself. We discovered that we had forgotten to learn our dog's name. Big Jim's orders concerning the care of his newly acquired treasure had taken so much time that morning that we left without the all-important name. Helpful brakemen suggested several we might use, but both Remus and I were young enough to remember mouth washings with strong soap, so none of the suggestions were followed.

"Well, he's Jim's dog," Remus decided, "so we'll call him Jim."

When Number Eight's hoarse whistle sounded a starting signal the big brown hound outdid it both in volume and tone. He had a voice like a foghorn. When the line of cars jerked into motion Jim ran circles around the pile of chains to which he was tied.

"You'll have to hold him," a brakeman told us. "If he gets any dizzier than he already is he couldn't follow an elephant in plain sight."

Hold him we did. For eight toilsome miles uphill; miles so steep the grade had to be relieved by switchbacks, we took turns holding Jim in place. Not once did that hound settle down or relax. He just didn't like riding flatcars.

For an hour and a half we clanked along. Always the track climbed upward. With each mile the late November air grew colder and we froze a little stiffer. Long before the Eight's whistle bellowed its signal for the top of the mountain, I was sure I knew why so few people in our town had never seen or known anything about snowshoe rabbits.

Jim was still howling his answer to the train whistle when we pushed him off the flatcar. His landing was soft, for he sank into nearly a foot of snow. At home only eight miles away the ground had been bare.

Before the log train was out of sight we two, with Jim at our heels, were plunging into the woods. Following Scotia Mike's instructions we took a right hand direction that would put us into Camp Five territory. We did not need the snow and cold to

74

tell us that Mike was right in calling Cheat Mountain "Canady gone astray."

With eight miles of upgrade behind us we stood in a different world. Gone were the hickory, oak, chestnut and poplar forests of our valleys. In their stead the somber green of spruce surrounded us. The sharp resinous odor bit at our nostrils and the cold wind made a soft sighing sound through the evergreen branches.

Interspersed through the spruce forest gray boles of beech and shaggy northern birch thrust straight trunks toward the light. Even low growing shrubs were different from those of our lower forest.

Such woods, we knew, covered the entire top of Cheat. To us it was a land of mystery, stretching five miles in width and forty or fifty in length. Since all the top lay above 4,000 feet in elevation with the usual cold and snow of such heights, it was not hard to understand that truly this was "a little patch o' Canady." Now with modern transportation the region has become a mecca for botanists and naturalists from far and wide. To us in that day of 1920 it was a land of fabled tales. A land filled with galloping white ghosts called jack rabbits.

Nearly all of this great stretch of northern forest was the private domain of the West Virginia Pulp and Paper Company. Along the banks of Cheat River the logging railroad ran. Along the same stream squatted the scores of logger camps which supplied the mill with timber.

Cheat River was an oddity in itself. Rising at the highest end of the mountaintop it maintained its channel for the full length of the long mountain ridge. At the point where we had topped the mountain a cut of fifty feet in depth could have sent the river tumbling down the eastern slope and diverted its final flow from north to south. It didn't belong up there, but there it was. Like a tightrope walker the cold trout-filled stream clung to its shallow trough on the mountain ridge.

Armed with our trusty single barrel shotguns; guns that cost all of four dollars each, and with pockets sagging from the weight of numerous black powder shells, we trudged into the forest. Jim followed obediently at our heels. He seemed to like the tracks we made in the deep snow.

There may have been an apprehensive glance or two into the more dense thickets. Cheat, we both knew, was the home of still numerous bears. Logger stories had never neglected that important resident. As for wildcats or catamounts their number was legion.

A half mile by an old skid road from the railway found us fairly in the cutover land of Camp Five. Vegetation consisting mostly of fire cherry, young spruce and blackberry canes struggled upward through rotting tops and branches of old slashing. Progress off the skid road wasn't progress. It was a hopeless fight. The abandoned skidway itself was no highway.

With three quarters of a mile behind us we stopped. Here we decided should be good territory. Certainly we were high enough, for we stood just under the top of Bald Knob, the 4,810-foot peak which ranked second highest in the state of West Virginia. Certainly there was cover. The slash and briers presented an almost endless brush pile. Blackberry canes were a favorite food of our intended victims and there were plenty of them, thorns and all.

One trouble presented itself. Jim seemed to have no inclination to hunt. Repeatedly we "sicced" him toward the thick cover but he just didn't "sic." He was perfectly congenial about the matter and wagged his tail good naturedly at all our instructions. To our excited "go get 'em boy" he turned a questioning glance but was content to let us amuse ourselves in our own way.

"We ain't found tracks yet," Remus observed. "Soon as we find some we'll get action. Big Jim says he's a born rabbit chaser."

Not more than a hundred yards farther we found them. Two boys stared in awe at those monstrous tracks. Rabbit tracks they were for certain but such as we had never seen before. Five inches long and half as wide those big hind tracks measured. Our minds whirled at the thought of how big must be the monster which made them.

I placed my extended hand over a track and remarked, "Scotia Mike said the tracks were big as a man's hand print. This one ain't."

"Likely this was a young one," Remus replied sagely. "But let's get him anyway."

Jim wasn't excited. Even when his nose was pushed into the tracks he merely sneezed away the snow. To all our excited orders he turned a calm and unruffled ear. Chunks thrown through the brush to simulate running rabbits got a bored stare. When we moved Jim moved. When we stopped Jim sat down. Two boys began to wonder.

"Big Jim lost his shirttail when he bought that dog," Remus said positively.

"And we lost our shirt when we borrowed him," I answered bitterly.

"Maybe he ain't acquainted with snowshoes," Remus ventured. "Maybe they smell different."

Young as I was, I knew better than that. Jim showed no sign of being a hunter. The woods meant nothing to him. Big Jim was just out twenty dollars.

"Well we can't stand here and look at that dumb mutt," I decided. "If we get a rabbit we'll have to kick him out ourselves."

Into the snow covered tangle of slashing we plunged. Jim was agreeable. He followed. Within a few yards the one lone track became a maze as others joined or crossed it and tracking was impossible.

Encouraged by the number of tracks we separated and began kicking at likely places of hiding. Jim chose to follow me. His choice was not flattering. It was downright discouraging to thresh through that thick cover and have to see that lazy hound behind me every time I turned around.

A half hour of lusty kicking brought me to a tangle of blackberry sprouts growing up through a spruce top. I gave the top a halfhearted kick and something moved from under it. Out across a fairly open patch shot a big gangling shape. I even remember seeing those big hind feet flopping. This was it, a sure enough snowshoe rabbit.

Taking a hasty aim I fired. A cloud of blue smoke fanned out before me shutting off sight of the rabbit. Not waiting for it to clear, I dashed through the screen. There thirty yards away the big rabbit lay kicking. No deer or turkey that I've shot since brought forth such a yell. I had killed the mythical Cheat Mountain rabbit.

Remus came running and Jim came walking. With that dumb hound staring in complete boredom we examined the trophy. Though not yet all white, he was a fine specimen. Splotches of grayish brown still clung to his sides, and his feet and ears were still in summer color. In size there was a letdown. The rabbit's weight didn't fit too well with past stories. Certainly he lacked a lot of being "jest a little less than Sambo," the bulldog.

The killing of a rabbit inspired everyone except Jim. With visions of a second kill Remus and I hunted hard. There was hardly a brushy tangle or fallen treetop that didn't get a thumping kick from one of us.

The rabbits were there. We began to jump them more frequently as we moved farther into the woods. Not all presented a shot, for in the thickest tangles those big boys could scoot under the brush like shadows and be gone before a shot could be fired. Jim, of course, remained neutral.

Remus got a bunny straightened out along a skidway and connected. His, too, was a splotchy mixture. November was just too early for pure white rabbits.

After two misses in thick cover, I killed a second snowshoe; this time a more nearly white one. Remus got his second a short time later. This, we agreed, was turning out fine. Four rabbits already were in our coats and we really had thought we'd be happy if we got just one. That would have been enough to prove their existence.

With the comforting weight of two rabbits in my coat, I moved along a side skidway. Under a fallen tree something moved and then stopped. The big eye of a snowshoe blinked. I bushwhacked him unmercifully. What a day this was turning out to be! Five down and the day young. Or was it?

In the midst of our examination of my third rabbit a hoarse whistle broke the silence. The log train was blowing at the top of the mountain and we were a mile away. In dumb silence we stared at each other. Finally Remus asked weakly, "What time was that train supposed to go back?"

"I don't know."

"What time is it now?"

I didn't know. Neither of us had a watch.

"How do we get home?"

I could answer that one. "We walk. And we better get started."

Plodding toward the railroad with Jim still using our trail, we called ourselves several uncomplimentary names. Only a pair of nincompoops would forget about time for catching a train.

"How far did you say?" Remus asked out of a long silence.

"Eight miles," I answered. "But we can save some by cutting across at the switchbacks."

The unevenly spaced ties made tough walking. We hopped, skipped and jumped as rapidly as possible. We knew well that darkness would be upon us before the long trek was finished, and to make it worse both of us realized that we were hungry.

Evening shadows were growing longer by the time four of the eight miles had been covered. Two miles back the last snow had disappeared and again we walked on brown earth. At the lower level it was, also, warmer, but that fact was scant comfort with another four miles before us.

At the halfway mark tragedy struck. We were plodding along in sour silence when something darted from the upper side of the roadbed and started across the track in front of us. It was a big groundhog, or whistle pig as we called him, which should have been in hibernation but wasn't. He was making a fast break for the lower side of the railway.

As the big chuck rolled his fat body across the track a miracle happened. Jim came to life. A dark streak came between us from behind and Jim was going for that critter like a bullet. Just as the groundhog reached the nearly sheer railway bank, Jim reached him. We had a blurred vision of the dog's teeth closing on the place where the pig might sit down. Then both went over the bank and out of sight.

Remus and I were just reaching the point of disappearance when a gray form went clambering up a tree trunk fifteen yards down the hill. I leveled my shotgun and fired. With a heavy plop the groundhog dropped to earth. But where was Jim? We heard no bark nor could we see him anywhere near the tree.

A faint scuffle in the leaves drew our attention to a spot directly under our feet. Down there at the foot of the embankment lay Jim. He was lying on his side and feebly kicking. We stared at the dog and at each other.

"You couldn't have hit him?" Remus gasped.

One glance at the tree base where the groundhog lay removed that possibility. Not only was the shot far over but was out of line. Besides he had been below the bank.

Quickly we slipped down the bank and examined Jim. Clearly he was not dead. He seemed paralyzed. We stood him on his feet but his hind quarters immediately folded under him. He refused to take a step or couldn't.

79

Across the small of Jim's back we noticed a black streak. A close look showed it to be charred wood. My glance took in the steep bank. Halfway up, there lay an old partly burned crosstie. It had been jarred loose from its bed of leaves and earth. On the upper end of it was dog hair.

Two great detectives came up with an answer. Jim had got hold of the speeding whistle pig and the heavy animal had flipped him off balance. His back had struck the crosstie with force enough to jar it from its bed. The blow left Jim helpless.

"If his back's broke we just as well shoot him," I said. "He'll die anyhow."

"Big Jim wants his dog back," Remus answered.

"Why?" I asked remembering Jim's hunting ability.

"I can't answer that," Remus told me, "but it's our hide if he don't come back."

It's our hide anyway," I figured, "when we take him home crippled."

"It was an accident," Remus said, "but who'd ever make Big Jim believe it? He'll swear we shot the mutt."

"We got to chance it."

Taking turns at the heavy task of carrying Jim we started down the railroad. The dog seemed to be in no particular pain. In fact I'm not sure he didn't enjoy being carried.

Two miles we carried that hound. We argued over who carried him the greater distance. We nearly fought at each change of the load. We decided, almost, to shoot him on several occasions. Each time the thought of Big Jim's anger started us on.

At the end of two miles an idea struck us. Why not make a stretcher. That way we could carry that hound between us. Quickly we cut two poles and fastened my coat between them. It looked like a good stretcher. It worked fine for twenty feet. Then Jim fell out. He hit the track bed with a loud yelp, and immediately got up walking.

I'll never know what that fall did for Jim. Maybe it put a displaced back again in place. Maybe it merely woke him up. Again maybe that lazy dog was just tired of being carried.

Within a hundred yards Jim began walking reasonably well. Within two hundred he had assumed his old place behind us.

The moon was shining brightly when Remus and I slipped that hound into his home yard. We didn't arouse Big Jim. Then late as it was, we made a beeline for the poolroom.

At the poolroom we became the center of attention. Marco Polo couldn't have received a better reception. We had brought home the bacon (not to mention the dog). An admiring crowd sized up every rabbit. A thousand questions were asked and answered. We felt like the heroes of the hour.

It was three days later before I saw Big Jim. Meanwhile news of our exploit had travelled. We'd actually brought in five of those mythical rabbits.

"Say," Big Jim rumbled, "you boys must have worked that dog of mine hard. All the next day every time he cocked his leg he passed bloody urine."

"Well, what do you know about that," I marvelled. "I reckon he just chased them long-legged jacks so hard his system couldn't stand it."

****

THIS BIGHEARTED BUSINESS

It happened many years ago but the pain of it lingers on. In fact every time I think of that incident, I feel like going out and eating grass with the other jackasses. But on second thought I don't do it for fear they wouldn't associate with me.

The time was June 1929. The scene was Little River in the upper part of Pocahontas County. The chief characters were a fellow named Remus, who was too lazy to fish, and I, who was too dumb to see farther ahead than my eyelashes. The tragic story was something like the following.

Glenville Teachers College had just closed its winter term and sent me home for a three month's vacation. As I crossed Cheat River on my way into the land of my nativity, the trout fever caught me. It was a bad case and nothing short of a week's cure on a good stream could remedy it. In that condition I received a letter from Remus.

According to his scribbled scrawl, the aforementioned Remus would arrive at my hometown inside of twenty-four hours. In the interest of future fishing conditions it would be well to spread the word among the trout so that a few could hide and survive to carry on the race. My company it seemed would be required since someone would have to carry the fish.

81

That letter solved my weighty problem, I dislike mentioning such things, but my financial condition was embarrassing and a week's camping trip would require a few odd dimes. Now, I figured that by carefully studying beautiful sunsets when bills were presented, I could graciously allow friend Remus to absorb all expenses.

The plan worked. In fact Remus arrived already equipped with supplies enough for a logging crew, among which was enough Pay Car chewing tobacco to supply a mountaineer spitting contest. Moreover, he possessed a car with a tank full of gas. I verified the gas situation before we started. Somewhere in my brain there was an unpleasant memory of a two-mile hike after a can of gasoline on a former trip with the same car.

Along with Remus came a fellow named Good. We promptly named him "Jim" due to certain resemblance to an undesirable character of that name. Since he has never seen the real Jim, no one has been hospitalized as yet. At home "Jim" Good was an immaculate bank cashier. On a trout stream he was a typical heathen. He didn't chew Pay Car—he ate it. The only thing I could figure on the tobacco score was that he swallowed it like a cow and could bring up a chew whenever he had a few tranquil moments to spare.

After the usual preparations of equipment and the usual number of things forgotten we were ready for the take off. As one bundle was pitched into the car there came the rattle of tin which sounded suspicious. Examination disclosed that some alleged joker had included in our supplies a half dozen cans of sardines. That's an insult to any fisherman.

After covering some twenty miles of good road we turned onto what had been described to us as a "fair strip of dirt." I wondered why the fellow who told us about it had such a happy grin on his features. Now I knew.

That road was one evidently made by the stone age residents of the state. And it had seen no improvement since. As Remus described it, "The only trouble was the ups and downs—up on a boulder down in a mud hole." We used chains, push power, and profanity. Before coming to the end of that trail, our chains were damaged, our push power was gone and the profanity was running low.

The "strip of dirt" brought us to a "last outpost" farmhouse. Here the so-called road ended. With packs on shoulders already tired from car pushing, we made the last three miles on foot. Right there I learned the limitation of a college education. Perhaps my head had absorbed a little during the past nine months but my muscles were sadly out of condition. I tried to use my brains to get the lightest pack but evidently Remus and "Jim" had more education than I. Consequently, when we arrived at the mouth of Little River, I was sweating under the heaviest pack and groaning over at least a dozen foot blisters.

But all sad things are forgotten when fishing time begins. With camp half set up, we made a break for the stream. The fever was strong. The water was right and the weather good. In fact everything was fine except the trout. Someone had insulted them. All were sulking in hidden spots. With wet feet and damp spirits we finished making camp.

As we were finishing up the little odd jobs around camp, three men and a mongrel dog passed by. One of the men carried on his shoulder a mattock, known in mountaineer parlance as a "whistle pig persuader." The other two carried four persuaded "whistle pigs." "Jim" eyed the dangling pigs and inquired as to what use would be made of them. The trio gazed at him in astonishment and answered to the point, "Eat 'em."

"Jim" was horrified. Remus was amused. I had an idea. While "Jim" spoke eloquently on the subject of "heathens who could eat such creatures" I took a .22 rifle and departed. An hour later I had a fine young groundhog dressed and salted without "Jim's" knowledge.

At noon next day after a fruitless morning of fishing "Jim" was carelessly informed that we had rabbit for dinner. He sure did like rabbit. He ate four pieces and looked in the pot for more.

After dinner "Jim" went to the river for water. Suddenly from that direction came a volley of profanity that would have shocked a marine sergeant. "Jim" had found my "rabbit" skin. He boiled for twenty minutes and simmered a half hour more. Before night he admitted that "the varmint was good."

For the next three days our trout luck was so poor that we caught ourselves wishing we hadn't left the joker's sardines. We figured fish would make a welcome addition to our menu. Remus had quit fishing. I believe I mentioned before that he was lazy. "Jim" had packed his tackle.

On the last morning of our trip which was Sunday I arose

early, determined to give those trout one last chance to repent of their stubborn ways. After walking a quarter of a mile upstream, I started fishing. The trout had undergone a complete change. They were striking like gentlemen. The beauty of it was that most of the strikers were large. All the children must have been sent to Sunday school.

Never in my many days on trout streams have I experienced such a day. Every pool meant a strike and the strikes were of such vigor that even a third-rate fisherman like I was, could scarcely fail to hook them.

My basket began to grow heavy. A trout under ten inches was scarce. They ran from ten to thirteen inches on the average. Such luck seemed almost too good to be true. Yet it continued until I was nearing the legal limit which was then twenty-five.

When my score was in the twenties things began to slack off. Strikes became fewer and not so hard. When I finally landed number twenty-five, my twelve pound basket was so full that he promptly slipped through the hole in the lid and landed in the water. It took a quarter of an hour to get another. The big feeding spree was definitely over.

When that catch was set down in camp, there was a two-way scramble for tackle. Remus and "Jim" went for the river as though their pants were on fire. They beat the stream with everything in their tackle books but the trout had quit. After a couple of fruitless hours, both returned. There were a few remarks about people who "just might have brought along a stick of dynamite" and other such insulting things, but in my grand, good humor I could overlook them all. I even carried the heaviest pack out to the road and did a horse's work pushing the car back over the "fair strip of dirt."

Now enters tragedy. Back at my hometown my big heart suddenly had a case of enlargement. Dear old Remus had paid all expenses. Dear old Remus was a fine guy anyhow. We were pals. Sure! Only one thing to do! Give that fine catch to my old pal to take home with him. I did just that. I felt as pious as a miser who has just dropped a dime and a pants button in the collection plate for the benefit of the African heathen.

Remus left me at my home on the outskirts of town and he and "Jim" departed. I supposed he'd go straight to his distant home.

Next week I went for a day's fishing close home. I made a

good catch and strutted through town with pardonable pride. An acquaintance stopped and peered into my creel.

"Good catch," he grunted, "but they're just bait beside that bunch Remus got last week." And he walked on.

For a moment I stood and stared. Then a horrible truth dawned on my feeble brain. That louse had shown those trout in town and left the impression that he caught them. Mentally I sputtered, "Of all the low down so and so's in the world of low down—." Interruption! Another curious one was peeping at my catch.

"Remus got a bunch a week ago that would make them look sick." And he was gone.

Five more people gazed disdainfully at my creel. Five more gave me a cool stare and remarked on "that bunch that Remus got." I was licked. My fishing reputation was at zero. The repute of Remus was at 112 in the shade.

Time wore on. Each successive catch of the summer brought reminders of "the bunch that Remus got." Never before did I realize what memories my townspeople had. They just couldn't forget "that bunch that Remus got."

At times I was tempted to tell that I caught those trout. But I didn't. In the first place it just wouldn't have been the sporting thing to do. In the second place no one would have believed me. Remus had the evidence—I didn't.

Near the end of the season, with my reputation still low, I took a farewell trip on a small stream. It was another "jack-pot" day. The trout were hungry and they were large. Twenty-three beauties lay in my basket as I returned home. They were almost as good as "that bunch Remus got." Maybe I had a chance to redeem myself. With great hopes I reached town. Surely memory would be dim by now and with that fresh catch I could again attain top rank.

The first person I met was one who on occasions "wet a fly," a good prospect. He looked at my catch. His face changed. "Jumpin' jackasses, what a bunch!"

My happy heart rang. Success at last! The admirer continued to paw through the creel. Compliments flowed like water. He was really impressed. At length the gentleman closed the lid and summed up with, "Yes, sir! by gum! That's a dandy mess of trout."

Then—just as my happiness knew no bounds he fixed me

85

with a penetrating stare and thrusting a finger against my chest roared, "But, look here, did you see that bunch that Remus got?"

My shoulders drooped; my head bowed wearily and I plodded slowly home. Now no one can say that I haven't been a good sport, for even in this writing I haven't told you the last name or even the hometown of the fellow who ate "that bunch that Remus got."

****

THE DAMNED OLD FARMER

Two hunters gazed with open hate at a prominent placard. "No Trespassing" glared back at them in black face type. One growled, "That damned old farmer ought to be made to eat every one of those signs and have the tacks rammed down his throat for a chaser."

That hunter was not an isolated example. He was Mr. Ninety Percent. If you are one of those folks who think hunters are plaster saints filled with the brotherhood of man and overflowing with the cream and honey of good sportsmanship, you are going to get hot under the collar when you read this. If you are one who realizes that there is something rotten, not in Denmark, but in the U.S.A., you are in for something designed to make you think.

To get right down to the core of the matter let us face a well-known fact. There are fewer acres of unposted land every year. Each year an enlarged army of hunters is crowded into a greatly lessened area. With the present trend continuing, it is easily possible that the day is near when the common man must sell his gun and bid farewell to his favorite sport. To quote our friend above, "That damned old farmer" will have put most hunters on the retired list.

In every sportsman's club meeting we hear the wail of "lost privileges." From the pages of every sporting magazine we read the sorrowful story of "American rights gone to hades." But in no instance have I yet heard or read a true analysis of the cause. "That damned old farmer" gets the blame and receives the hate and venom of the sporting fraternity.

"Farmers don't post land. Hunters drive the nails for ninety percent of the trespass signs in America." That remark was made by a farmer friend of mine who after twenty years of enduring the destruction wrought by trespassers finally tacked up the forbidding signs. He estimated that it had been costing him two hundred dollars a year to allow people to use his land in pursuit of game. His trespass damage bill was equal to his tax bill.

That farmer was putting the blame right where it belongs; squarely on the shoulders of irresponsible hunters and fishermen. He was not a lone example. Dozens of landowners to whom I have talked give the same answer. In almost every instance the story has been the same. "I was forced to post my land. Hunters just won't respect my rights or property."

The tale of woe varies but little. The chief complaints are fences thrown down, livestock killed, crops damaged, property stolen and in many cases even the lives of the farm family endangered. Total lack of appreciation also comes in for a share of the trouble as does game hog tendencies and the worst offense of all—pure vandalism.

One farmer gives an example. He had neatly stacked two thousand feet of lumber valued at two hundred dollars. A group of hunters drove a rabbit beneath the pile. Pitching the lumber indiscriminately right and left they routed the bunny. When the farmer later discovered the deed, rain and sun had warped and twisted the disordered boards to such an extent as to cut their value in half. That rabbit cost him one hundred dollars! He posted his farm.

On one farm where I have long enjoyed fishing privileges, I found new trespass signs. Inquiry brought this story. A carload of fishermen too lazy to walk to the stream drove their car across a twenty-acre field of ripening oats. On their return they made a wide sweeping circle not even following the first tracks. The owner estimated his oats damage at fifteen bushels plus the trouble of cutting over the crushed down circle.

One hunter that I know has posted three farms. In each instance a different offense brought out the signs and lost for himself and others the right to hunt.

Near my hometown four hunters went onto a farm. Within a quarter of a mile of the farmhouse they slaughtered six fine domestic turkeys. Wild turkey season was not in and six would have been beyond the limit. In court they claimed they thought they were shooting wild turkeys. In reality they were simply stealing turkeys. That farm is now forbidden to hunters.

Personally I own two tracts of land, each in a different county. They are not posted. I don't want to post them. But I fear the day will come when I have no other choice. My annual trespass bill includes fence repairs, stolen fruit, chickens killed by dogs, destruction of trees and other things of more or less importance. In almost every instance my known desires concerning my property are ignored by those who use it. Very frequently I find myself reaching for writing material or telephone to order those pretty black and white signs.

Both in my own experience and the reports of other landowners, I find that the one element that creates more resentments than any other is the outright vandalism of those who go onto property of others. Willful, deliberate destruction certainly doesn't sound well in connection with sportsmanship but it is surprising to find how much of it is done by those professing to be sportsmen.

Let's look at some examples. One farm, well known for its squirrel woods, is now closed to hunters. A group of city "sportsmen" finding the game not stirring amused themselves by shooting the windows out of a farmhouse which chanced to be vacant. Another place was closed because deer hunters found the weather vane on a large barn roof a nice target for their rifles.

One farmer found a group of hunters using rails from a pile for fuel. He informed them that the rails were valuable and requested them not to burn them. The campers became incensed at the reprimand and just before they left on the following day threw all the rails on their fire. They made a nice bonfire but the farm is now posted.

The examples I have given are not from a single community. They represent items from several sections and from more than one state. They could be multiplied hundreds of times over in every state of this country. If any reader requires further proof let him interview the farm owners in his region. They'll back me up.

Now as our army of sportsmen find themselves facing those familiar signs, a howl of anger goes up from coast to coast. Refusing to concede that they themselves have driven the nails in most trespass notices, hunters and fishermen demand to know, "What's going to be done about it." Let me answer. Until the sporting fraternity takes its own proper steps nothing is going to be done about it.

We may shout state ownership of game resources until we are hoarse. The farmer will still say whether or not you collect it on his land. Tell the landowner this is a free country! He'll agree with you and add that he's free to post his land.

Dozens of articles are printed on the subject of getting friendly with the farmer. The week before opening day is fine for making those friendly calls and passing out those friendship cigars. Don't kid yourself, brother. The farmer can tell those three for a nickel stogies as soon as he smells them, and he can spot hypocrisy in your friendly advances as soon as you've said, "Good morning."

The extremists are loud in their demands that the state pass laws to prevent land posting. Brother! That's out! Property rights are among the bases of our Constitution. To forbid a landowner the right of controlling his own land would require a fundamental change in the organization of our government. Remember too that a law removing property control rights of a farmer might also affect the city. It would be hard to find a stopping point.

Trying to pass laws giving all the right of using private property is a hopeless and senseless dream. Farmers still know how to fight in more ways than one.

An old Negro preacher who had been pelted with tomatoes and eggs during his sermon made the following announcement at its close.

"We shall now have a special song by the choir. Then the collection will be taken. Then Brother Johnson will pronounce the benediction. Then stick around, folks, and you'll see the damnedest fight you ever laid your eyes on!"

Something similar will happen when laws making trespassing legal are passed. When some hunter tells some farmer that said farmer can't put him off his property, I want to stick around. There's going to be "one of the damnedest fights you ever laid your eyes on."

In this entire game we had just as well recognize that the farmer holds the aces and the joker as well. Legislation is out. The agricultural industry is more powerful in our government than the sporting fraternity. Gripe and grit your teeth and swear to your heart's content. When it's all over "that damned old farmer" will still be calling the plays.

Is there a solution? If so, what is it? In my opinion there is and this solution has found favor with every farmer with whom I have talked. It is not simple but it is possible. Also it may be very bitter medicine to a large number of people. However, bitter medicine sometimes cures serious ailments.

In the very beginning the sportsmen of our country are going to have to recognize and accept their own blame in the matter. When *we fully realize that land posting is chiefly an outgrowth of abuse by hunters and fishermen we will have made the first forward step.* Once the disease germ is identified the doctor is in a better position to effect a cure.

Next I would suggest a little schooling in the subject of property rights. We who go afield on the domain of another must be made to realize that the land is not free but that it is undeniably the private goods of the man who has paid for it. His deed, backed by the governing power, says that it is his, to have and to hold and to use as he sees fit. Those acres of woodland belong to the owner as inviolably as your radio belongs to you. They are his property in as complete a sense as your suit of clothes is yours. It is as reasonable to say that you have a right to hold a club meeting in the front room of an unwilling city neighbor as to assert that farm property is free to all. The golden rule in paraphrase might well be used at this point. "Do unto the property owner as you would have done unto yours." We might add, "Think in regard to property of others as you would have others think in regard to yours."

Most important of all and most radical of the bitter cure is passage of *stricter* trespass laws! That may sound foolish. Certainly it is in direct opposition to the demands of most sportsmen. Let us examine the possibility of the idea.

First, such a step would greatly reduce the damaging acts of irresponsible hunters and fishermen. Trespass regulations with real teeth, enforced by state agencies, would make the careless think well before committing offenses. If the fence breaker knew in advance that there was a strong possibility of his paying the price of his damage, he might not be a fence breaker. If the hunter knew that going onto forbidden land might well bring him into more serious consequences than the mere wrath of the farmer, he might be much more careful to obtain permission. In short, severe regulations would reduce the number of offenses against property and lessen the antagonism of landowners.

In addition, such measures would put the issue more squarely up to the hunter. They would form a mandate that said, in effect, "Be a gentleman and act with decency or you suffer the consequences." Under such conditions sportsmen and outdoor organizations might well spend more time educating their own irresponsible element and less time demanding legislatures to give them the green light on farm trespassing. In time the offenders could be largely singled out and either taught better or prohibited the use of the fields.

The second and greater effect of severe trespass laws would be to give the farmer a sense of reasonable security. As it stands now in many states the landowner has no active protection against the trespass nuisance. State agencies do little or nothing to assist him. Should he decide to take legal action he must go himself and secure a warrant paying for the writing of it from his own pocket. Then after seeking out a law enforcement officer who serves the order he must be his own prosecutor in the justice court. On conviction the guilty one is fined maybe twenty dollars and costs. The justice and arresting officer take the costs and the bighearted state takes the fine. The landowner goes home to repair the damage at his own cost.

Such weakness in trespass regulations has led to the posting of much land. The owner posts in self defense. He wants every precaution because he realizes that his property protection rests largely on himself.

Farmers with whom I have talked are fairly general in their agreement that they would be more willing to allow sportsmen on their land if they had a reasonable protection from the state. They ask for laws requiring payment for damage. They want strict regulations concerning killing of livestock and careless shooting around farmhouses. Above all they want the trespass regulations to be enforced by the state officers as a regular part of the law enforcement program. A landowner seldom worries about a hunter in whom he places full confidence. If laws and enforcement agencies could give him a feeling of confidence that his property was under good care, might we not have more open land?

In my final words I should like to suggest one more step, an

91

important one and one of long range proportions, that might assist in solving our posted land problem. This step is recognition of the true worth of the American farmer. I don't mean the cigar passing visit of false friendliness, I mean for city, town and country alike to move away from the contemptuous "damned old farmer" attitude.

Today in no walk of American life can we find a finer, more versatile or more courageous class of citizens than is found on our thousands of farms. The American farmer is fine in that he is tops in friendliness, hospitality and true neighborly spirit. He is earnest, religious and sincere. He believes in brotherly love and the friendly hand of assistance. He is the staunch foundation of a nation whose cities are recruited from the farm.

The farmer is versatile in that he must know and do a wider variety of tasks than any other walk of life. He is at once laborer and mechanic; builder and chemist; executive and worker; home founder and citizen of the nation.

In the heart of the farmer lives a courage that knows no defeat. Unafraid he faces the threat of drouth, storm, heat and cold. He fights against an endless army of plant diseases and insect pests. He may be knocked down but he comes up fighting and steps into the battle again.

Yes, Mr. Sportsman, "that damned old farmer" is a mighty fine man.

****

JUST APPOINT A COMMITTEE

Somewhere between the covers of that great old book that gathers dust in so many modern homes we find a queer story. It seems that the early Israelites occasionally felt the need of ridding themselves of an accumulation of bad conscience. Perhaps they had been caught worshiping the golden calf or charging too much interest on a loan. Whatever the offenses might be the resourceful chosen people knew how to get rid of the pangs of conscience. They unloaded their sins as methodically as a fox unloads fleas by taking a dip in the water.

The first step was to procure a good healthy goat. Then each member of the congregation placed his hands on said goat's head, thereby signifying that he was making the poor critter a present of all his sins. As soon as all members had thus cleared their consciences the scapegoat, as he was named, was booted out into the wilderness and left to bear his burden alone.

That little custom gave the word "scapegoat" to our language. Today we no longer use the "odorous billy" for such purposes. We have found a better goat. Modern man being more humane uses "the committee."

The advantages of such human scapegoats is readily seen. A true goat can't understand profanity which is directed at him; a committee can. The original old billy couldn't use his brain to secure soft advantages for others; a committee must do just that. The greatest advantage lies in the fact that every interested party is supposed to be allowed to kick the committee around at will. If you'd try that on a real goat he'd place his forehead on your fanny with sufficient force to drive you through a couple of brick walls.

Aesop tells us an interesting little tale concerning an assembly of rats. It seems they met to devise ways and means of disposing of an annoying cat. A proposal was made from the floor that a bell be placed on the troublesome feline to warn all of his approach. The motion having been duly recorded and passed by unanimous vote, an old killjoy rose and demanded to know who was going to put the bell on the cat. Aesop must never have finished that fable, at least he never did let us know how the job was done. But I'll bet my last fishhook that I know the answer. They appointed a committee.

A few years ago some of our brethren found that too many people were descended from the *Mayflower* sailors. It began to look as though there must have been a "helluva" crowd on the boat. In an effort to get ahead of the "Joneses" some of the thinkers claimed to have descended from our good friend the monkey. Such claims immediately raised a row—among the monkeys. Indignation meetings were held in every fashionable jungle and various courses of action decided upon. The matter would have gone hard with the human race but for one factor. Monkeys are of notoriously short memory. They forgot which ones had been placed on committees.

The committee has been the loafer's salvation and the answer to a chiseler's prayer. Under our present system of committee peonage the lazy members of any group or organization can

93

enjoy all the advantages of such alliance and never lose their nonstop loafing records. Such loafers can always rouse themselves from hibernation long enough to yell, "Appoint a committee" every time a project of any sort is proposed. Then they lapse back into a coma until the fruits of the committee are ready to be enjoyed.

Sportsmen's clubs are famous for committees. We have committees on game, committees on fish, committees on forests and whatnot. I understand that some of the more up-to-date clubs have a committee on the appointment of committees.

My own experience as a would-be sports club enthusiast bears many scars which may be termed committee marks. Being naturally of a rather feeble mind I have never had adequate protection against such appointments. When other members of keener wit were escaping membership on the "committee for possum propagation," my slow mental processes were so far behind that I was appointed before I knew what the committee was for. In fact I haven't found out yet.

Now that I think of it I was really on a lot of sports committees before I knew the word. An older brother used to take me fishing occasionally. On these occasions I was invariably appointed to dig the worms, therefore, I suppose my first activity on these lines came through my services on the "Fishworm Committee."

That brother should be a business executive. He was a wizard at appointing committees. When we arrived at the fishing hole, we often built a fire. There's where I got on the "Wood Gathering Committee." While I gathered wood, he set out his half dozen cane poles in the half dozen best places in the hole. By the time I was ready to fish most of the bait was used and all good locations occupied. However, loving brother consoled me by saying it didn't really matter who caught the fish. Main thing was to have a mess for breakfast. Furthermore I was to have a special honor that evening. At home I'd be appointed to the "Fish Cleaning Committee."

The only time I ever knew that big brother to put himself on a committee was the time I caught two bass and lost a third before he got a bite. He put himself on the "Bait Conserving Committee," and limited me to dead minnows.

When sportsmen throw an annual banquet, the committee appointer is in his glory. The meeting before the occasion finds

94

all dimwits like me present. All committee dodgers are tied up elsewhere. Just couldn't make it. We have an entertainment committee, a committee on table arrangements, one on food, another on decorations and a free air committee to provide speakers.

Each little "beaver" so appointed works like a woodpecker in a petrified forest. When all is done, he surveys his work with pride and waits for the flowers. There must have been a hard freeze for no flowers show up.

The appetites gather. The food disappears like a late April snow. Mr. Committeeman, who was in charge of serving, gets a chicken neck and a cold potato out in the kitchen. But he's happy in the knowledge of a job well done.

Then we do a little eavesdropping. This is what we hear.

"Decorators sure didn't hurt themselves on this hall."

"What a messy table arrangement. Must have done it blind-folded."

"Ain't this rotten food? Who in hell was on the food committee?"

"Where'd they get that windbag they call a speaker?"

We wait to hear no more. With a silent vow that never again will we be on a committee, we start to sneak out. But we can't miss the last loud remark from a "meeting a year" member.

"The whole damn thing's lousy. We ought to appoint a good committee to supervise the dopes."

Now in case you don't like this brand of article just mail your protests on a penny postcard. If there are enough protests to justify it, I'll appoint a committee to investigate rotten magazine contributors.

****

SO HELP ME—IT'S THE TRUTH

Someone once said, "If you do one act that the world cannot forget you have really accomplished." I have really accomplished. I once won an obscure "Liar's Contest." It was only a little contest and it only took a little lie to win, but the world cannot forget it. From that day to this I have been a marked man.

If I meet an acquaintance on our town's only street and say "good morning," he looks at the sky before he answers. Once I told a fisherman his boat was sinking and he sat right in it and drowned.

For a truth loving person such a reputation is a decided handicap. Even truth loving people like to harvest a little personal glory, and I know of no better way to reap said glory than to keep the admiring world posted on one's own masterpieces of accomplishment. "Blow your own horn" has been a popular adage for more years than Methuselah lived. However, since that fatal contest I can't seem to get by with any horn tooting. It would seem that in a world where practically everyone uses up most of his spare time blowing his own horn that surely I could get by once. But I can't. With the whole world blaring out a million tales of personal glory from trumpets six feet long, I can't get by with a sneaking Jew's harp solo.

In discouragement I have almost given up telling of the most remarkable things that have befallen me. Many a time some golden experience is right on the tip of my tongue fairly clamoring for a hearing and I just close my pretty lips like the petals of a cabbage and say nothing. If I could ever get back on a par with respectable folks, there would be a hundred tales I could tell that never have been spoken. You see the world is the loser by my silence.

Maybe you didn't guess it but this is all a build up to the fact that I'm going to break over and tell one of my unpublished and seldom spoken experiences. Right after it happened I may have mentioned the matter a time or two but after no fewer than a hundred listeners had winked furtively or slipped away from me in the manner reserved for dangerous lunatics, I grew discouraged. Then once a man to whom I had truthfully recounted the tale remarked, "That ain't no lie. That's a stupendous prevarication." I felt vaguely uneasy but still flattered by his remark until I got my hands on a Noah Webster's little book. Then I quit telling the story altogether.

Now Ed Johnson has just informed me that he wants a trout story. He also adds that it had better be good. Otherwise he'll publish the name of a certain guy that missed a buck last fall less than thirty yards away and is still wearing his full length shirt. All right he asked for it.

On a certain Monday morning in June one of the red gods
96

pulled my ear until it hurt and shouted that the trout should be biting. Furthermore he suggested that West Fork of the Green-brier might afford a few of "bragging size."

As the red gods direct, I do. Before noon I had two fellows for company and in an ancient Model T was on the way to the stream. Each one of these companions has threatened me with legal action that will leave me standing in the street clothed in nature's costume if I ever connect them with any of my "durn tales." (That objectional phrase is theirs, not mine.) To safe-guard my shotgun, single suit of clothes, hound dog and minor items of property I shall not use their names. They shall merely be Bill and Bud. Why shouldn't they be? That's what we always called them.

For a few miles our darling little Lizzie Ford chugged along like a contented coffee grinder. Then the blank blank so and so began to act up. First she began to sputter. Sore throat without a doubt. A few adjustments around the battery box cured that. Next a rear tire suffered a serious rupture. A patched tube and an old leather boot top for a reliner persuaded it to try again. A mile more and Lizzie developed kidney trouble. Without so much as holding up one finger she began to leak all over the road. Examination disclosed multiple breaks in her radiator system.

Here now was a task that required the services of an M.D. (Doctor of Mechanics). No first-aid job would serve. Somewhere we had heard that a few handfuls of horse manure would stop radiator leaks but we didn't have a horse along. Searching dili-gently we found where one had been. The remedy didn't work.

The matter finally ended by filling the radiator and a bucket. With one of us riding the running board and holding the bucket we made a dash toward the next water. The carried bucketful served for a drink between springs. Nine springs and two swamp holes later we reached the end of the road.

After an invigorating and blister producing hike of four miles, we reached camping grounds. On the way in we had noticed a "punky" (gnats to you) flying ahead of us. He was a trifle smaller than a bat. At our campsite we learned why he had thus flown ahead of us. He was the Paul Revere of the whole punky tribe. Aroused by Paul the entire clan met us in full force, wild for fresh meat.

There was just time to set up camp amid that itch producing

97

swarm before daylight faded. Between scratching we cooked and ate supper. With a smoking chunk from the fire we routed a blue billion punkies from the tent, closed the flaps and hit the hay. Did I say "hay?" I meant solid earth.

I won't go into details concerning that healthful night's sleep. I'll leave it to the poets to rave about the sighing winds in the spruce trees, the soothing lullaby of the frogs and all the other pleasant sounds of a night in the open. But I will say this: If there were any sounds that night I heard them. Maybe it was a touch of insomnia. Then came the dawn.

All the unpleasantness of the world, even punky bites, can be forgotten when a bright June sun is peeping over the hills and looking at its own reflection in a sparkling trout stream. With my feet feeling the tug of rushing water and my ears full of the song of the stream I soon forgot such things as balky Fords, hard beds and sleepless nights. Even Bill's flop at making the breakfast pancakes was nothing more than a slightly unpleasant lump in my stomach.

The trout were in a playful mood. They acted as though they might be interested in playing hide and seek. At almost every pool and ripple there was a rise. But those rises were not strikes. They were more of the nature of exploratory trips to the surface. Seldom did a trout actually touch a fly. Having in this manner seemingly detected the fake they were satisfied to rest quietly on the bottom.

Here and there a fish not so well schooled as others would actually take a lure. Even in such cases it was difficult to make a catch for the strike lacked the proper enthusiasm. Noon found me with a rather small catch, but I was not in the least worried. At least I was learning that plenty of fish were present. Besides that, I had another day yet. Tomorrow they would surely be hungry.

Noon found me beside a beautiful pool. The kind your day-dreams paint during the snow locked days of winter. Here the stream had been checked in a forward rush by a sheer cliff several feet high. In making a rather sharp turn to glide along the base of the cliff the waters had gorged out a deep hole, then leaving its depths had fanned out into a broad shallow. In the center of the deepest part of this pool a large rock rested; a perfect home for an old hermit of a trout.

For several minutes I laid trout flies over that pool with great expectations. Imagine my surprise: no rises. Things were not going right. Almost every other spot thus far had shown trout. Now this perfect gem failed to produce so much as a flash of color. Could it be possible that trout didn't know a good home when they saw one?

A cheese sandwich in my pocket needed some alterations, so I sat down on the bank and began the task. The bread was a trifle damp, having been dunked once, but the cheese still held its shape very nicely. While I was eating my somewhat soggy mess a large raccoon came cautiously along the bank. He stepped into the water and while his eyes seemed to un- concernedly explore the sky his black forepaws expertly probed beneath a flat rock. The first rock netted him zero, but the second was more productive. From beneath it he drew, in a clenched paw, a huge crayfish. Holding his prey in one paw he industriously scrubbed it with the other. Thoroughly washed, the crayfish was eaten with great relish.

There's no sense in this world at times. There I sat, griped because my sandwich was wet and at the same time that fool coon was fairly scrubbing the shell of a crayfish that had spent its entire life in water.

The coon, having lunched on two more crayfish, disappeared. I finished my sandwich and rejecting the idea of a few crayfish for dessert gathered up my rod preparatory to moving on. With no expectancy whatever I flipped my fly over that pretty pool. And then it happened.

Here's where I fool you. You expected the next sentence to be "Wham! Socko! Bam! A half ton of trout hit that fly like a charging elephant." That is what most stories say but I'm truth- ful. Here's what did happen. As my fly drifted past the rock in the pool a long shadow rose slowly from the depths. Without any evidence of hurry it moved to the surface; a beautiful rain- bow; three pounds at least. Still unhurried he inspected my fly. Then lazily returned to the depths. Do you feel let down? So did I.

For the next two hours that pool got a beating such as it never had before. More flies and assorted lures skittered over its surface than it had formerly seen in a year. Every live bait known to the region had at least one representative drowned in those green depths. But the big trout slept on.

At camp that evening I found myself the black sheep. Both

Bill and Bud had made good catches. It seemed for a two-hour period following noon the trout had struck in earnest and during that spell they had made near limit catches. There were expressed suspicions that I had been on some warm bank asleep at that important time. I denied the charge but, somehow, forgot to mention the Big One.

Morning of the next and last day of the trip found everything favorable. Bill and Bud having made good downstream yesterday were bighearted enough to go down again. With the discouraged air of a dying martyr I started upstream. Out of sight my dying martyr guise disappeared and I fairly made the gravel fly getting up that river. A quarter of a mile below the pool I began to fish, just to see what they were striking. The answer was nothing, at least nothing I had.

When I reached the haunt of the big one, my catch was zero. When I moved on upstream after trying all my lures, it was still the same. However, there had been one bit of encouragement. While drifting a copper spinner over the pool, there had been a visible flash of a trout's side in the shadow of the big rock. Maybe later he'd get serious about it.

I had reached a point about half a mile above when the fish began to hit. One of those eating moods seemed to have struck them. When the feed started I had just put on the copper spinner in place of a wet fly. Before that, I had been using two flies, and changing only the end fly and had left a black gnat on the upper loop. Not at all professional of course, but the trout didn't seem to mind. They struck regardless.

When three real beauties were safely in my creel I realized the fish were really feeding and my copper spinner was the magic trick. I turned and started fishing down. In eagerness to get back to the big one I fished rapidly but in spite of that I arrived there with nine fine trout. The larger two or three were "bragging size" in any man's language, but the big one was still in the river.

Very quietly I came into the fast water at the head of the deep hole. I dropped the spinner into the swift current. Holding the line just enough to keep the copper plate whirling against the current I allowed it to be carried slowly downward. As it approached the big rock I became tense. Somehow I felt that this was the time. The lure reached the rock, carried past it and on down. No "Wham," No "Socko."

100

The spinner was carried toward the shallow water at the tail of the pool. Just as it reached a point where the failing current nearly ceased to turn the blade there came a sudden strike. For a second I felt a wild thrill then I saw the fish; a beauty of a brook trout, hooked solid, but not the big one.

Feeling the bite of the hook the brookie headed toward deep water which was also toward me. Three feet below the big rock he stopped short and drove across the current. The leader cut the water and for a flashing second I saw the forgotten black gnat flash over the surface. The next instant it was engulfed by a vivid arch of color from the shadow of the rock, and the big rainbow fought with the smaller brook trout.

My spine tingles today when I write this. That fight remembered has given me a thousand thrills. And when I shall be too old to wade a stream I'll still enjoy life just recalling it. When I was a very small child, I saw Halley's Comet. To me it appeared a bright vivid flash in the sky trailing a long fiery tail. That's what those two fish called to my mind. Wherever the rainbow went the brook followed. Fight as he would he was still trailed along like the tail of a comet. The rainbow being on the upper lure, fought both me and the smaller trout. Tugged at from both sides he still cut more figures than Sonja Henie ever dreamed about.

For my part I, too, was in a spot. Behind me flowed a swift rush of water. The right-hand bank was a sheer rock. On the left alders bordered the stream so thickly that beaching was impossible. The only place to land those fish was below the pool. That's where we went. Though I skirted the bank as closely as the brush would permit I still ruined tobacco in my hip pocket. It didn't matter. I'd have waded to my neck for that catch.

On a sandy bar ten yards below the deep water I finally beached those two scrappers. Two more beautiful fish or more brilliantly colored I have never seen. Of course, fisherman like, my three-pound estimate of the rainbow was too much. Combined, the two weighed three pounds and one ounce with the rainbow furnishing two thirds of the total.

Now go ahead and mutter your nasty remarks about people who can't help lying. That was my greatest trout fishing thrill, and so help me, it's true.

101

****

DIARY OF OLD SPOTS

Before I get through with this tale some doubtful Thomas is going to call me a liar. But I should worry. They laughed at Columbus and Bob Fulton didn't they? The day may come when this article goes down in the history of literature as the most unusual biography of all times and places. So you doubt it do you? Well, so do I.

I never would have gotten the material for this famous tale if I hadn't been born with ultrasonic hearing. That's one of the consolations for being of the lower type of animal life. Dogs and monkeys have the same quality. They can hear dog whistles that can't be heard by other folks. Then it stands to reason they can hear a million other sounds that escape ordinary ears. Personally, I refuse to admit that a monkey has anything that I haven't except a tail. Fleas will even leave a monkey to get on me. That ought to prove something.

With ultrasonic hearing I hear a lot of things that normal people miss. For example I have often detected hiding rabbits by hearing their heartbeats. I can locate a deer a hundred yards away by hearing him bat his eyes. Once one of Cal Price's panthers waylaid me but I escaped by hearing him lick his chops when I was still two hundred feet away.

This marvelous gift of hearing has made it possible for me to hear the language of fish. That's how I got the life story of Old Spots. Oh, so you don't believe fish can talk? Well, Brother, they can! With as many fishermen on the streams as we now have it's a simple matter for a fish to gather and use a complete vocabulary. There's one trouble with their speech. In these days of poor catches a lot of what they pick up is of a profane nature. Many a young trout has had his mouth washed with gravel for repeating what some fisherman said just after his boot slipped on a round rock.

But to get back to my tale. One June evening I crept quietly to the edge of a deep pool where I knew Old Spots had lived for several years. Just as I made my third cast over the pool my ultrasonic ears picked up a thin voice. It seemed to come from the water. Then I understood the words.

102

"Hello, sucker, how's tricks?" The words came clearly from the center of the pool, and there, lolling on the surface lay Old Spots himself. He had one fin to his nose and was waving it, first at me, then at my floating fly.

I was so dumbfounded my eyes popped out like jawbreakers on sticks and my mouth gaped until my chin rested on my second shirt button. Old Spots laughed and rolled on the waves. "Shut your mouth and pull in your peepers, dope. You look as though you were hunting snipes with two lanterns and a wool sack." And the old devil laughed uproariously at his own joke.

When I could finally speak I rather stiffly suggested that there was a pronounced lack of politeness around that particular pool and suggested that visitors be treated a trifle more courteously. Old Spots sobered, and looked at me in amazement. He even brushed a fin across his eye to make sure he was seeing correctly. Then again he spoke.

"Well, I'll be—. So you can understand me? I'd about given up hope of ever getting anything across to you bat-brained guys that come along here. How did you do it? Are you Superman?" I modestly told him about my ultrasonic hearing and Old Spots nodded comprehendingly.

Within a short while that big trout and I were as chummy as two fleas on a dog's ear. Old Spots seemed to enjoy talking and now that he had someone to listen he fairly bubbled over with enthusiasm. It was during the course of this conversation that the great idea of writing Old Spots' biography was born. I have made no additions or omissions in the story. It is written just as Old Spots gave it to me.

"My parents," Old Spots began, "were of the finest old families in these waters. My father was of the Spring Branch trout family and my mother a descendant of the famous Roaring Fork clan. After their marriage they built their little love nest near the big rock, just below the old leaning sycamore tree. There I was hatched. There were exactly two hundred and eighty-four of us in the family and the old folks were mighty proud of their brood.

"My memories of that first year are rather vague, but I shall never forget my second year when I entered school."

Here I interrupted. "Do you mean to tell me fish go to school?"

Old Spots gave me a pitying glance then dashed aside to gulp down a huge grasshopper that had just misjudged his landing field. "Listen, Mullet Head," he said, "have you never heard of a school of fish? Why we fish were going about in schools when your dim-witted ancestors were still conking each other with coconuts. Why, you two legged jokes of the animal kingdom copied your schools directly from us. Didn't even have enough originality to change the name."

I nodded meekly and after glaring at me for a moment Old Spots continued his story.

"That school of mine was really something. We were taught by an old trout that had been here so long he had stolen bait from the bone hooks of Hiawatha. These modern youngsters don't know what school really is. In those days we really got an education."

Again I interrupted. "What kind of courses did you take in school?"

The old trout answered promptly. "Astronomy, meteorology, navigation and self defense. They're all good subjects and the really educated trout must know them all. Take astronomy for example. If we didn't know all about the increase and wane of the moon, how could we feed and act in accordance with your present day fisherman's calendar? We must know to the day when the moon is full and when the new moon appears. We even have to know certain hours of the day when one planet crosses the path of another. Don't you know that it is useless to fish during any hour when the shadow of Jupiter is cast over any part of Mars?"

I admitted that I didn't know that fact and Old Spots snorted in disgust.

"I suppose you don't know that meteorology has any bearing on fish?" he queried.

"Oh yes," I answered, "I'm familiar with all the angles of that subject. In fact—"

"Stop it," interrupted Old Spots. "I can see by your face that you're lying. In fact," he added mournfully, "you fishermen just can't help lying. I wouldn't trust the word of any one of you as far as I could throw a mule by the tail. It's lucky a fisherman didn't write the Book of Jonah. He'd have had Jonah swallowing the whale."

My face grew a trifle red but I said nothing and the talkative fish went on. "In meteorology we learned all about air currents,

104

storm centers and barometric pressure. We fish were masters of all such science a full thousand years before the apple cracked Isaac Newton on the cranium. The educated trout now plans all his meals and formulates his menu in accordance with barometric and thermostatic conditions."

"What did you learn in navigation?" I asked.

"Rudimentary things," answered Spots. "Swimming, leaping waterfalls, breasting currents and the like. Of course we paid some attention to speed of water currents, ebb and flow of waves and effects of whirlpools. These were all important in the matter of judging the proper lead to take on a floating fly or in making the proper current calculations when taking a minnow in midstream. But in the main navigation was a primary course."

"But self defense! Now there was a real study. And only the brilliant ones mastered it. Hours without end we worked under our old teacher learning the gentle art of self preservation. The first lessons were easy. We passed exams on avoiding turtles and killing water snakes with comparative ease. Then came the tough assignments!"

Here Old Spots paused as though thinking back over old things and I had to remind him to continue.

"What were the tough assignments?" I asked.

"Food identification," he answered. "Some teachers were satisfied if their pupils could tell the difference between real and artificial food, but not my old professor. He made us memorize the names of all artificials. Before I left that school I could tell a Royal Coachman from a Queen of Waters with only a split second glance.

"Opening day of fishing season was our test day. That day we lined up across the old Round Rock Pool and called the names of the various patterns as they were dragged across the surface. I was perfect on flies but the old professor really jarred my teeth when it came to spinners. I identified a Colorado number one as a Slim Idaho. I'll remember that crack on the head to my frying day. You see I was allowing my mind to wander a bit when the question came and knowing that both Colorado and Idaho were western states I momentarily confused them and called out the wrong one."

At this point Old Spots began to strut up and down the pool. "Before I got through that exam," he stated, "I was so good that the professor was allowing me to branch out on related material. I identified eight out of ten lines by makers' names and only missed the trademark on three pairs of boots during the whole day. My crowning achievement came when I distinguished the difference between a catgut and a nylon leader. There really was a trick in that one. The catgut had a tendency to drift nearer to us, attracted by the odor of fish."

At that point I began to think that Old Spots had caught something from fishermen besides the English language but I wisely made no comment.

"Yes, sir," he continued, "I owe my long life to that schooling. If I hadn't learned my lessons so well there I might long ago started growing three inches a year in some fisherman's tale. As it is I'm the oldest trout in these waters and still going strong."

"Have you ever married?" I asked.

"Been married more times than a movie star. Have descendants in both forks and every tributary of this stream. Didn't you read that crazy report last year of a salmon run in this stream? That was no salmon run. It was just my family gathering for our annual reunion."

At this point another fisherman came splashing up the stream, and Old Spots turned to look at him. Then turning to me he made his final speech.

"Just look what's coming. Got every article the tackle stores sell. Carrying everything but the kitchen sink. He couldn't fool the dumbest sucker in the river. However, I'll have to drop out of sight. If he'd chance to see my seven pounds he'd probably die of acute excitement. So long now, dope."

****

PEOPLE CHANGE—ALIBIS DON'T

A not too happy father stood before a not too proud family. Pop wore a loin cloth about his middle which failed to hide his hairy chest and made very public his parentheses legs. His matted hair hanging over his sloping brow proved beyond doubt that the barber pole had not yet appeared in his neck of the woods. In one hairy fist he clutched a heavy club.

Mom showed traces of feminine refinement. Her hair was

done up in the very latest fashion. A cute set of bangs added to her appearance and also hid a few odd club marks which were probably treasured relics of her courting days. A skirt effect of tanned deerskins hung at a rakish angle from her ample hips. Her upper anatomy was covered by a lovely coat of tan. The children, all nine of them, wore a variety of smiles and scowls.

Pop waved his club savagely in the air, "I tell you, I had that bear dead to right. I had him backed into a corner of a cliff where he couldn't get out except by coming past me. When he started I raised my club and just as soon as he was in reach I swung on him with a lick that would have killed a mastodon. But just as I swung a branch caught my club and turned it aside. I missed him by inches. Before I could get in another lick he was in a thicket and gone."

Mom turned wearily to a daughter. "Warm up the acorn soup," she said, "no meat as usual."

One of the male offspring winked at his brother, "That's the fourth time the old man's used that alibi during this moon." His whisper was just a trifle loud and next moment he was howling like a wolf and holding both hands to a very bright and rosy bottom.

Pop glared at the other members of his family circle to see if any more remarks might be forthcoming. None came and Pop stalked into the family cave.

This little incident occurred in the Finnish Bogs in the year 9870 B.C. Yet with very slight variations that ancient alibi, used so successfully by old Stinko Clubslinger, is still going the rounds today.

There are interesting points of comparison between the ancient and the modern. Note for example the weary look on Mrs. Stinko's mug. Then watch the same weary expression cross the features of modern Mrs. Nimrod as friend husband relates, for the fourth consecutive year, how a twig deflected his bullet and prevented the family from feasting on long promised venison.

Also we could find many modern chips off the old blockhead that could testify to Pop's reaction on having his alibi doubted. Many a one might recall that warming stinging sensation near his tailbone that came as a result of youthful sarcasm concerning the old man's well-prepared story.

Down through the long ages hand in hand with the hunter and fisherman have come the ancient excuses. In each new age they wear a slightly new dress, but take off the dress and the same old skeleton grins out at you. At the same time when Mark Antony was telling Cleopatra, "Kid, you're different. You really are a fairy queen in this moonlight," some Roman fisherman was blaming the moon for his own poor fishing skill.

America as usual is tops even in alibis. Take our early Indian. He had them all beat. Before going on a hunt he recited a long-winded chant before the altar of the hunting god. If he missed a single word or spoke one sentence out of order he'd have no luck. Since the chant was as long-winded as a politician's speech, he had plenty of chances for mistake.

What a priceless alibi! There was no blame on poor shooting, no reflection on stalking skill, no blundering mistake on his part. All our red brother had to do was come in without game and with regretful sighs remark that he must have left out a couple of "ugh's" in his chant and all was explained and forgiven. Perhaps old Professor Sock-in-the-wash got out the hunting primer and made young Hound-With-Hanging-Ears recite his ritual a few times but that wasn't bad. At least no one winked or whispered remarks about poor grade liars.

Our pioneer ancestors had some pretty good ones. Wouldn't it be nice if we could come in and casually remark, "Just as I had a bead on that deer, an Indian tomahawk whizzed by my ear. It didn't make me nervous but it blurred my sight for a second, and danged if I didn't miss that buck."

Great-great-granddad also had a good one or two in the peculiarities of his gun. Wet powder was good for a few misses up to ten days after a hard rain. "Long fire" was a favorite too. Sometimes the old musket fired the cap and the slow-burning powder in the tiny powder tube failed to reach the main charge until after Great-great-granddad had lowered said musket and was reciting a few words not taught to him by the circuit rider. Then it probably fired unexpectedly causing the old gentleman to jump out of his brogans and requiring a more vehement renewal of his unorthodox devotions. But annoying as the long fire was when it really occurred, it still made a dandy alibi for failure to bring home the venison.

Such good alibis as these have had to be discarded along with old Dobbin and the family buggy, but most of the old ones are still with us. Now and then some inventive mind comes up with a new one but they are scarce. Therefore, the modern American

Walton or Nimrod finds himself using a set of time worn, if not time honored, little white lies.

Now here is the reason I write on such a subject. A serious situation has arisen in the sporting world. To put it briefly; practically every sportsman's wife and nearly all the boys at the barbershop are becoming too familiar with those old be-whiskered "reasons why we didn't get 'em." Even Junior shrugs and grins as he remarks to himself, "Wonder why Pop doesn't break himself of that nasty habit of lying?"

There are two underlying causes for this situation. The first is apparent. There simply are not enough alibis in circulation. With the speed of our modern day they get around too fast. Today Mrs. Murphy hears that her husband would have got that turkey if his ammunition had been any good and tomorrow she learns by back-fence grapevine that Mr. Mulrooney failed for the very same reason. Yet each was using different brands and on the same day she finds that old "Possum Face" Wheeler got his turkey at sixty yards using shells exactly like those friend husband had. Something begins to smell and it's not roast turkey.

The second reason for our deplorable state is the lack of system in the use of our alibis. We get in a rut. One or two good ones get us by for a few times and we fall in love with them. Unconsciously we use them until they are worn thin at the seat and threadbare on the elbows. When the boys at the barbershop hear for the eighth time in one season how it was too cold on the ridges for squirrels to stir they become mildly suspicious. The "better three-fourths" may believe once that it was too dry for grouse stalking but even she knows that it can't stay dry forever. Besides that, she may wonder why the downpour that fell three days ago didn't extend into the nearby woodland.

Now the problem facing every hunter and fisherman is what are we going to do about it. Well, I'll tell you. To begin with we are going to have to get down to brass tacks and hard work. The sportsmen of America are going to be compelled to put the old brains to work and think up some new alibis. We may as well face facts. The old story of how our gun failed to fire is out of date. That bullet glancing off the bear's rounded skull was old when Daniel Boone was a baby. And blaming the wind has been used so long and enthusiastically that wives are beginning to talk of harnessing the wind for the world's future power. Yes, brother, new alibis must be created or we are going to see the day when we'll have to come home and say, "Sorry, dear, I missed him."

Along with the creation of new material we simply must have a "share the alibi plan." When you get a good one pass it on. A good suggestion would be to have them printed on small leaflets. Hardware stores could do a wonderful service by enclosing one of such leaflets in each box of shells or each dozen trout flies. By using, say a dozen different sets, they could institute the "surprise prize" system. Sportsmen undoubtedly would make more purchases hoping to obtain a complete set.

Some have suggested that the Department of Natural Resources should supply "a few good reasons for failure" along with license sales. However, it is the opinion of this author that such an undertaking would require too much time and expense. Besides that factor, most of our state commissions are so busy trying to think up alibis for their own failures that they have little time to devote to the interest of others.

Let us assume that we do succeed in creating a new set of easily swallowed lies. Or if not a new set at least a revision of the old ones. Remember that the second cause of our trouble was repetition. In this line let each outdoorsman get for himself a small notebook. One that can be carried in the vest pocket would be preferred, for it must never be seen by improper eyes. In fact it should be a very private affair.

Once a suitable book is obtained all acceptable alibis should be written therein. A rough index at the beginning will prove helpful. For example, Mr. Hunter has spent a fruitless day rabbit hunting. Before going home he glances at the index. There it is under the "R's." Rabbit failures—page 60. He turns to page 60. This one is selected from a dozen. "Leaves too dry—dog couldn't hold trail." That one will do.

Before going home Mr. Hunter will do another little task. On each page of his book there is a blank margin. With a pencil carried for the purpose he will make some such notation as, "used this one November 18, 1966." Now he is in no danger of repetition. The well-filled alibi book should carry enough that there be no need of using that same one for at least two years.

A final word of caution may not be amiss here. It concerns hunting or fishing parties. Before the party breaks up, the alibis should be selected and agreed upon. Sometimes one will serve

110

an entire group. For example, if the "water was too high" for one, it stands to reason all of a party could use the same and by a united front even make it more convincing. We can readily see how such an arrangement would be more satisfactory than for one to use "too cloudy" and another of the same party to use "sun too bright."

At other times separate reasons must be selected. If Mr. Jones failed because he was "compelled to fish downstream" it would never do for Mr. Smith to fail because he was "compelled to fish upstream." By simple logic we can see that not more than one of a party should fail to get his buck "because of danger of hitting a stray cow." The old standard of "wrong size shot for the game" should never be used by two or more using different sizes.

With these helpful hints the great American sportsman should be able to restore himself to a marked degree. However, he must use care. There are many pitfalls in his path. For my own part I fear my plight is too hopeless for repair. It was all due to one error. In advance, I prepared myself a book such as suggested above. It disappeared from my pocket. The loss was a complete mystery until a few nights ago when I chanced to hear my wife, a fisherwoman, say to a few friends, "That bass would have weighed nine pounds and only one thing kept me from landing him. There was a flaw in that darn leader."

****

BUSINESS BEFORE BASS

Ever since my sister got married, I've had a brother-in-law. Having a brother-in-law is not unusual but that fact doesn't keep Arch from being unusual. He's the kind of guy of which you only meet one and he's it.

When my sister first acquired possession of Arch via the noose of matrimony, she, as befits a member of a fishing family, was already a dyed in the river fisherwoman. He had never held a fishing rod in his hand and still thought catfish were canned fish for cats. Our whole family, all thirteen of us, felt that his education had been neglected and with haste set about correcting his defect. You see, we felt that the family would be held in contempt if it became generally known that we had acquired, even by marriage, a nonfisherman.

Thought of that process of education still leaves me with a feeling of increased age and general debility of the nervous system. Not that Arch wasn't willing to learn: he was even mildly enthusiastic. The trouble was that he was already the proverbial old dog and new tricks were still hard to learn.

Out of kindness of human feelings I'll skip briefly over the education of Arch. Imagination may suggest what a healthy family of West Virginia hillbillies can do to one who is innocent and willing to come back for more. Suffice to say that after numerous long trips, many hundreds of foot blisters, a score of nights spent on hard ground, and a few duckings in deep pools, along with sunburn, mosquitoes, gnats and profanity, we, the professors, felt that our pupil was actually gaining ground. And to make it better he had really caught a few small fish. As a matter of course Arch always swore off fishing forever and tried to sell us his tackle after each trip. That was the most encouraging thing about him; it showed he had the makeup of a fisherman.

All this leads up to a September evening when I wasn't in a pleasant mood. The reason was that frost seemed to be in the near future and I had a couple acres of uncut corn. In spite of a lifelong aversion to work I had manfully determined to cut corn all day Saturday. Friday evening Arch drove into my backyard.

The fishing fever had my dear brother-in-law in its grip and he was ready to take a chance on one of my trips.

"Where can we fish tomorrow?" he asked, pretending he couldn't see that corn.

"Can't go," I answered. "Gotta cut corn."

"How long will it take both of us to cut it?" asked Arch, sticking his neck out.

A big demon, or maybe it was a little one with big ideas, entered my thoughts and presented a dirty idea. Flesh is weak. Adam fell. Why shouldn't I?

"Oh," I answered carelessly, "two of us should cut it out before noon. Then we could give the Big Eddy a once over in the afternoon." I didn't believe two of us could cut that corn in less than a full day.

"We'll be at it at daylight," announced by bighearted helper.

Daylight found us in that corn patch. Arch worked like a

112

horse. To keep up appearances I tried to keep up with him. If we'd been fighting fire or ants in our pants we couldn't have worked harder. By noon the sag in my carcass had filled all spare room in the seat of my pants. I was going on will power alone. At 12:30 the corn was done. I only longed to go to bed.

By the time we had eaten dinner the sky had clouded and a cold wind had started blowing. The signs pointed to a very poor evening for fishing. Hopefully I suggested to Arch that the weather seemed bad. Arch didn't seem to realize that weather had anything to do with fishing. He listened to my opinions on bad weather and looked me over with a sort of gleam in his eye. Immediately I decided it would be a grand day for fishing. I forgot to mention that he's a lot bigger than I am and a couple of years older.

Not until 2:30 did we find ourselves at the Big Eddy, one of the finest bass holes on the Greenbrier River. We had a bucket of crawfish for bait. Most people apologize for using bait so I suppose I must. In the first place it was too windy for artificials. In the second place it was too cold. In the third place I'd rather use crawfish in the first place.

The sight of the dark water, waving under a cold wind didn't suggest any record catches of bass and my expectations were small. Arch didn't seem to share my lack of zeal. He acted as though he expected to catch something.

Our first half hour and our best soft-shelled baits netted a couple of chubs. That was more than I expected. Then I caught a bass. That was an interest-rousing surprise. The first was just a thirteen incher but in our waters that is a good one. Here a sixteen-inch bass is one to tell the neighbors about and an eighteen incher is something to carry around town and weigh in all the stores. Of course we have fishermen here who regularly tell us of their four and five pounders, but all communities have liars.

With a bass to our credit we fished more earnestly and soon Arch had a hefty strike. When he set the hook things happened. Line went off his reel like magic and the rod did some bending that strained its backbone. Arch got a wee trifle excited. Among other things he stepped on a round rock and sat down hard in two feet of water. When he got out of his bath the fish was still with him and now Arch put the power on his reel handle, perhaps the science of fishing was not perfectly observed but in

113

a few moments there skidded onto the bank a bass to make my eyes pop. Eighteen inches of length and over three pounds of weight.

Since Arch had never caught a bass that might even be called a big one you could scarcely blame him for the way he acted. You could overlook his chest expansion and even understand it when he announced that he was satisfied for the trip. I humored him into trying for more.

With that big one to Arch's credit my stock didn't look so good and since his fish was larger than anything a guy had a right to expect in that water I had small hopes of coming in on the glory. But believe it or not within fifteen minutes I had hooked and landed one so nearly the same size that it would have required double lens glasses to find any difference at all between them. They were perfect twins.

From then on every nibble was a potential big one. Luck held. My next strike netted a nice two pounder. One fit to be called a big one on any other day but this. Arch came in again with a nice one weighing over a pound.

Within a short time two more both of good size reposed on our string. Then the fish refused to cooperate further.

With seven bass totaling twelve pounds we were satisfied to call it a day. Both of us were tired. Come to think of it we had been on the verge of collapse when we started. For some reason we hadn't remembered that while the bass were striking. Now on the mile long tramp to our car we were once more reminded that our morning of corn cutting had left us none too fresh. However, I didn't mind a few sore muscles. My corn was cut; we had a good catch, and unless Arch reads this he'll never know that I didn't think we could finish that corn cutting job in time to go fishing.

****

SO I WENT CRAZY

Now please don't misunderstand me. I'm not griping. In fact, I'm usually happy. All of us screwballs are happy. It's only when we have rational periods, like the one I'm having now that we are really sad. And I believe that telling my true story to the world will relieve me now.

It all started from such little things that everything seems a trifle confused. But as I gaze out through the bars of my well-padded cell and view the peaceful autumn scene, my thoughts (if a lunatic can have thoughts) seem to settle on four sources of blame. To these four sources I credit my present mental state. They are: George Washington; a man named Ananias; my mother's teachings and the fact that in early youth I became an ardent hunter and fisherman.

Had it not been for that last item about the hunting and fishing, I might have been able to withstand the mental strain. In that case I'd now be a respected citizen, earning my own living and holding membership in some exalted fraternal order. I might even be a town marshal or teacher of a Sunday school class.

It all started when I was only a few years old; too little to defend myself. My mother thought I was born to be a president because I looked like Abe Lincoln's coon hound. Therefore, she undertook to train me in ways of honesty and veracity. Little did she realize that in such a condition, I'd be a total loss as a politician.

Among other things my mother did, she told me about George Washington. That lovely tale of little George killing mamma's colt, and manfully admitting it, made a tremendous impression on my plastic mind. The famous cherry tree followed suit and fired me with a crusading zeal for truth with all the trimmings.

I must admit that the story of the cherry stump had one setback. Mother had recently set a nice plum tree in the backyard. Dad had given me a new pocketknife. Some unknown person had told me that a ring cut around a tree would cause that tree to die. Enough said.

Mother discovered the circled plum tree early one morning. I was out of bed running about in my nightgown. At the first question concerning the fatal circle I proudly admitted my handiwork. The spirit of George was strong upon me. Mother for the moment had forgotten the paternal ancestor of our nation. I went across her knee. My nightgown came up. Here I draw a merciful curtain, but right there I resolved that, although

115

naked truth is good, from that day hence forward I'd tell it with my breeches on.

After the noble lessons from the life of Washington my mother brought some buzzard by the name of Ananias into the picture. It seems that he's a Bible character who stood right up and told a whopping big lie. Before he had that fib well off his chest, he got knocked dead in his tracks. Now I was certain I'd tell nothing but the truth.

The wheels of time rolled on, and as I said before, a mighty love of rod and gun entered into my being. By now I had outgrown my presidential ambition and figured Buffalo Bill was a better ideal by many miles. Mother even admitted that maybe I was meant for the penitentiary instead of the White House. However, in spite of all, I still clung to my resolve to be a Washington in statement if not in fact.

Even before my sporting troubles began, I had a vague feeling that all was not well with the world. For some reason I was always a mediocre person. Never could I reach the great heights of perfection attained by others no matter how good I thought I, or something of mine was. My neighbors were, or had something, much better. They were always on top of the heap while I reinforced the foundation.

For example, if I chanced to tell about the two-pound tomato I grew in my garden, someone else had grown one of four pounds and ten ounces. I related the fact that I got fourteen eggs a day from my eighteen hens. My neighbor came back with a gloomy reply to the effect that his hens were not doing well; only getting twenty-four a day from twenty-five of the loafers. I was quite proud of my cow which gave five gallons of milk per day but Bill so-and-so had one that gave eight per day in bad weather and filled a washtub when conditions were right.

From such incidents I should have been warned, but I suppose my mental makeup was never strong. At any rate I went at the hunting and fishing game with childish simplicity. No kind friend advised me. No inborn instinct protected my innocence. I hunted and I fished. I told of my successes. I gave weights and measurements. I used accurate scales. And —— *I told the truth.*

Now remember, I don't claim to have been the only truthful sportsman in the world. Maybe I was simply a mediocre person. Be that as it may, it was not long before I began to have queer feelings inside me, and to think that all was not well with the

116

world. Furthermore, I believe there may be others who will agree with me.

For instance how would you feel in my shoes. I got a nice twelve gauge shotgun. I found that I could knock a gray squirrel off a tree, at thirty-five yards. I was elated. I told about it. I got, not congratulations, but pitying glances. Not one of my acquaintances would even mention any shot with the scatter gun of less than one hundred yards. In fact, it appeared that one hundred yards was standard for all guns except mine. I ask you, how would you have felt?

With my rifle it was the same. When my once trusted 30-30 knocked a buck over at one hundred fifty yards, I thought it was good and I was pretty fair myself. But before the season ended, I discovered that my buck was the only one in the county killed at less than three hundred yards.

The only way I could account for that deer coming so close was that he was young and innocent. On standard scales he tipped just 138 pounds. All those killed by other hunters were mature. None weighed less than 250 pounds, and none had horn spreads of less than three feet. Speaking of horns; that was another evidence of the extreme youth of my deer. His horns only spread eighteen inches.

Not long after the deer episode a wild turkey fell to my poor grade shotgun. He was a neat fourteen-pound gobbler. Proudly I carried him through the old hometown. The Nimrods looked him over. One remarked that it was a fair turkey for a late hatch. Another figured he might be an offspring of the thirty-eight pounder he himself had killed in the same woods a week ago. Others inquired as to whether there were any more in the same nest. I slipped out and buried my poult so no more people would discover that I had killed such an infant.

After such setbacks I turned to squirrels. There is little difference in their sizes and I felt that surely I could compete for honors in such a field. However, my limit kill meant nothing. Fifteen to twenty seemed the score for all acquaintances in spite of the legal limitation of four. The same held true when I tried out on grouse. I hung my gun up for the season. It seemed the safe thing to do. Already I felt mental disturbances coming on.

During the latter half of the winter I lived in seclusion. By spring I felt that my mental qualities were once more strong. I even looked forward to a summer of fishing with enthusiasm. Little did I dream what fate had in store. Innocently I listened to stories of the local Waltons. I heard of places where the fisherman had to hide to bait his hook. My fancy thrilled at reports of eight-pound smallmouths. The old lunkers that lived in certain ponds thrashed through the foaming water in my dreams.

Then came the time when I was free to fish. The places where it was dangerous to carry bait in the naked hand netted me a bad case of sunburn. Hours of patient effort failed to bring so much as a strike from the traditional lunkers. I even suspected they were not at home. Finally I did get a three-pound bass.

When I lugged that fish in, I thought at first that I had finally reached top rank. Every fisherman came to see him. Each one weighed him. Each one measured him. Then each one told of the six or eight-pounder he had caught and departed.

The last one to see my fish was an old fellow named George Washington Smith. Gravely he looked my prize over. Then gravely he commented, "Not bad, but last week I ketched two that totaled jest twenty-one pounds and four ounces."

So I went crazy. Something seemed to snap in my head. The scenery whirled for a minute, then cleared. When the dizzy minute was past, George Washington Smith was going down the road making twenty feet at a jump with my solid steel casting rod wrapped three times around his neck and with the reel in his mouth. In my mind the features of the father of our country were fast fading away and soon were replaced by the grinning mug of that horrible example, Ananias.

As yet no one suspected the change in me. I still had my freedom and might have still had it had not all my efforts at beating Ananias at his own game backfired. The failure of those very efforts is what made me a dangerous maniac.

Let it be understood that I was now in my weakened mental state determined to be the biggest of liars. I had reached the conclusion that though Washington was the father of our country Ananias was the father of its citizens.

My life became a nightmare of failure. Too long had I been a disciple of truth. I served an ostrich for dinner, called it a turkey and invited company in. Before the meal was over, the keeper of the local zoo arrived in company with the sheriff and I served sixty days for the stealing of one ostrich.

118

While in jail I developed a plan for using a set of wire stretchers on a bear hide. I figured I could make it do twelve feet. Then I chanced to read in a book something about an old-time queen named Dido. It seemed she had stretched a bull hide big enough to make it surround the site of the city of Carthage. I discarded my idea. I knew that if Dido could pull a stunt like that in the old days some of the modern stretchers I knew could make a bear hide cover the Great Lakes.

As soon as I got out, I went to work again. I put magnifying lens on my camera and photographed a fish. A fly chanced to be on the fish and looked the size of a buzzard so no one believed the picture. I seined a trout stream for a big catch and got caught by the game warden. That cost me one hundred dollars.

My next effort got by for a while. I grafted elk horns on to the head of a brown cow and called it a deer. For two weeks all went well and I was beginning to believe it myself. Then some fellow stole my head and sold it to a museum as a prehistoric monster.

There was no originality in springing the hands of my fish scales by eighteen pounds. I thought an old one might get by. Before I got a fish to weigh, my neighbors borrowed the scales and became famous overnight. Their newborn son weighed twenty-eight pounds.

Discouragement was riding me hard. I was about ready to quit. Then came inspiration. I soaked my tapeline in alum water. Now, I figured I'd get some real measurements. My wife chanced to pick up my tapeline. In the presence of two town gossips she measured her hipline. Next week she was granted a divorce.

There was just enough left in me to try one more trick; an act of desperation. I loaded a shotgun shell with nitroglycerine in hopes of making one of those long shots. When I fired, the barrel wrapped around my neck, the stock knocked my front teeth out and the trigger guard killed a chipmunk (just a small chipmunk) fifty feet behind me.

Next day I reported to the asylum. I could fight off violent spells no longer. They put me in this padded cell where I can do myself no harm. I'm happy here. My guards are fine fellows. Soon one will come in bringing my lunch. Then I'll tell him about the twelve-pound bass I just caught in the rubber wash

119

basin. He'll whistle in amazement and say, "Holy cow! That's a record for this season."

****

AIN'T WE PECULIAR

All outdoorsmen have their little idiosyncrasies. My chest feels much relieved. Ever since I learned that big word I've had a burning passion to use it. Now just to be sure, I repeat, all outdoorsmen have their little idiosyncrasies. I won't use it too often. I'm afraid I can't spell it more than six times.

Webster says that jawbreaker comes from an equally terrifying Greek word, which same I wouldn't repeat for fear of getting my mouth washed out with lye soap. However, in spite of Webster, I believe there is an idiot in the woodpile somewhere. The first part of that verbal monstrosity has a familiar appearance. It sounds and looks like what Dad used to call his seventh offspring when said offspring was caught sawing nails with the new handsaw or keeping pet frogs in the new stone churn.

Then, too, just look at some of the things sportsmen do. Call them "idiosyncratic" if you wish, but there are times when it appears that good old "idiotic" would be a lot nearer the truth and much easier to say.

Exhibit "A" is Simon J. Flushpocket. Simon proves Barnum's statement of a fool being born every minute. He reads all advertisements and nibbles at every baited hook that is hung out for suckers. Sunday afternoon he sees an ad for a new "indispensable" for sportsmen. Monday morning his check for $67.59 is in the mail. Friday he becomes the proud possessor of a gadget that stretches tent ropes, cooks beans, skins catfish, scares off "punkies," and cures snakebite. It weighs only 72 pounds and has only one drawback—it won't work. Saturday morning he throws the whole family in an uproar raving about cutting expenses. Reason—his wife just bought a new fifteen-cent can opener.

Exhibit "B" shows us the portrait of Mr. Ailing. He's the doctor's meal ticket, and the drugstore's greatest blessing. To hear him tell it his lumbago is torture and his rheumatism something out of this world. Figuratively speaking he's standing with

120

one foot in the grave and the other on a roller skate. A strong draft or a few drops of moisture would make his wife eligible to collect insurance.

But the opening day of trout season rolls around. The rheumatic joints of Mr. Ailing have splashed through two miles of icy water before dawn. With numb fingers he strings a frozen worm on a hook and peers through the falling snow for a hint of sunshine. However, he's not looking for health rays in the sun. Old Sol would merely make the fish bite better.

Exhibit "C" is a classic work of nature's art. So numerous is he that it wouldn't be safe to name him. Let's just call him Mr. "C." This gentleman three times a day, sits down to his table upon which his wife has spread excellent food. For her pains she is informed that the steak is under done, the potatoes too heavy and the biscuits have too much crust. Furthermore, the coffee is weak and the cherry pie too sour.

Next week Mr. "C" goes camping. For six days he dines upon burnt fish, slightly tainted before cooking, fried potatoes, fried eggs, fried bread, fried onions, fried beans and fried bacon. All these are seasoned highly with bugs, stray worms, flies, dirt, cinders and fish scales. Each greasy mess is washed down with coffee from a rusty bucket which also has its share of "forest seasonings." The drowned and "multi" boiled rat which was found among the grounds on the fifth day probably added more than his share to the taste and aroma. On returning home Mr. "C" secretly takes a dose of Epsom Salts and between nonchalant trips to the bathroom wearies his wife with tales of "real camp cookery."

Exhibit "D" is a real economist. Let's watch him in the local butcher shop. With gimlet eyes he inspects each piece of deceased cow. He informs the poor butcher that his prices are high enough to enter heaven's gate on a downhill glide. After insisting that all bone be removed he finally buys a beef roast.

At home that night exhibit "D" grumbles about meat prices until he destroys the beef roast appetite of his entire family. He concludes the dinner with the yearly prediction that as soon as hunting season opens there'll be free meat on the table.

November proves his prediction. The family has one scanty meal of grouse and two of slightly tough squirrel. Later in the month the happy circle meets a new dish that Junior refers to as "mangled rabbit." Splintered bone and numerous number six

121

shot prove that Pop "hit him all over." However, Junior saves the shot to use in his air rifle and that saves money.

All of Mr. "D's" friends hear of how he's hitting the high cost of living. And sure enough four or five meat dinners at the expense of Mother Nature do cut down on the store bill.

But let's take a look at the other side. It reads like this:

Time lost for hunting	$ 65.00
New hunting clothes	32.00
Ammunition	2.00
Transportation	14.00
Liniment	1.00
Damage for shooting one sheep	18.00
Total	$132.00
Cost per pound	$ 19.76

Nevertheless exhibit "D" is happy.

Now may I editorialize a bit. The peak of the average hunter's idiosyncrasy lies in the attitude with which he spends his money. He pays $75.00 for a shotgun, ditto for a rifle. He shakes loose from $100, or more, for hunting clothes. His transportation bill is enormous. Ammunition costs him $10.00 to $20.00 per year. Then when all is said and done he kicks both walls and the back end out of his stall at the mere mention of charging more than $2.00 for a hunting license. In short he pays more for each item on his purchase list than he spends to supply himself and the future with fish and game.

Pardon me now I'll have to stop. I must rush down to the hardware store. I hear they have a dandy bunch of secondhand rifle reports for sale. Also I must get a new frying pan for my next camping trip. Nothing like that old camp cookery.

✳✳

KINDRED SOULS

Ed Coran stood on the shore of Lake Matewan with the glory of a Maine sunset flooding about him, and breathed the pine-scented air in deep, almost sobbing, breaths. It seemed too good to be true; this newfound freedom of his. He was afraid that at any minute the glorious beauty of the scene would fade into dark stone walls, the sweet air become the foul breath of the prison, and the gentle sighing of the pines merge into the harsh tones of the warden. But the waves lapped on at his feet with their soft musical sound and the evening breeze continued, with soft waving motion, to sway the dark green blanket of pine. Thank God! It was not another prison dream. He was actually here; in the heart of God's world. The freedom he had dreamed of for five long years was his at last.

Bitter years had those five long stretches been. Bitter had been each day from the time he entered those gloomy walls, sentenced on a trumped-up charge preferred by an enemy. He did not think now of that enemy; he had been dead for two years, but he did think, with seething hate, of the prison, the wardens, and the social order that permitted a man to be thus imprisoned. Freedom had been Ed's dearest possession and he loved and reveled in it with a savage joy. Freedom, to him, was the keynote of life. Prison had not killed but only sharpened his love for the great outdoor world. Now as he thought of the past he felt that he hated mankind.

Three days previous Ed had been liberated and a friend of former years, knowing him to be an outdoor man and realizing that a summer in the open would restore his health, had secured for him this position as collector for a city zoo. And now as he stood on the lakeshore and watched the guide and canoe that had accompanied him fade from sight he seemed to realize, for the first time, that he was actually free. For a time he contemplated the glory about him, drinking in the beauty of the scene as one dying of thirst drinks sweet spring water. He forgot all save his new found freedom, forgot that he must arrange the camp equipment now lying about the beach, forgot all physical needs in the exotic enjoyment of nature. Darkness was falling before he turned to the task of making camp and preparing supper.

That night Coran was reluctant to creep into his blankets. Sleep seemed a waste of time. It seemed so much more worthwhile to sit up and listen to the plaintive love calls of the little red screech owls or the gurgling of the waves on the beach. At last, however, he rolled in his blankets wrapped in a peace and joy he had not known in five years and was soon lulled to sleep by the lullaby of the pines.

The sole purpose for which Ed had been sent to Lake Matewan was to capture a magnificent bald eagle for the zoo. For

123

years Old Whitehead, as he was called, had made the lake country his home. No man had ever been able to capture him, and he reigned an undisputed king of the air. From tip to tip his huge wings spread ten feet and his body measured three feet from beak to tail tip. He had no mate, but lived a solitary existence about the lake. To see him soar above the waters like some ancient bird of the Olympian gods was a sight one would never forget. He seemed a part of the great world; something that gave the final touch to the grandeur of the place.

Coran soon had the haunts of the great bird mapped out. Day after day he watched him wheel aloft and carefully noted the places in which he was accustomed to alight. Each tall dead tree or high flung rock was a station for Old Whitehead. It would be a simple matter, thought Ed, to place traps in each of these places and capture the bird. But he was a mistaken man. He had not counted on the uncanny wisdom of the eagle.

For two weeks the traps were placed in the favorite perches, so skillfully concealed that Ed, himself, could scarcely detect them. Each trap was as carefully avoided by Old Whitehead as it would have been had it been in plain view.

Coran tried baits, but the bird passed them all by. He laid cunning snares, but all to no avail. Every trick Ed knew or could devise was tried and still the eagle continued to sail the air as of old.

Ed constantly studied the bird and as he observed him he could not help admiring the huge bulk and amazing flight. His unsuccessful trapping was, in itself, a tribute to the wily brain of the eagle. And so as time went on and the unsuccessful attempts continued Coran began to regard the bird with the respect one feels for a worthy foeman.

Occasionally Coran had noticed Whitehead flying overhead with a rabbit or other small animal in his talons, and he wondered why he would not take his baits as readily as he took food from the forest covers. Then the answer struck him. His baits were not alive. Why had he not thought of that before? Live bait! That was what he needed.

Without delay Ed set about making rabbit traps. The great snowshoe hare was plentiful in that section and it was only the work of a couple days to capture a half dozen. These he fastened in "cubby" pens with his traps at the open side just far enough out to be out of reach of the rabbit. Whitehead visited all the places where the sets were made, but touched not one, and daily caught other rabbits in the forest. Live bait was a failure.

It happened that a favorite pastime of Old Whitehead was that of robbing the great ospreys, or fish hawks, as they are called, of their fish. Ed had often watched the performance with keen pleasure. Perched on some tall snag or cliff the wily bird would wait until an osprey, from his perch on a lower limb, would dive into the water and come up with a struggling fish. After allowing the captor to get sufficiently high from the water he would swing into pursuit and soon make the hawk drop his burden. Before the fish could hit the water Old Whitehead, with his wings folded and dropping like a meteor, would snatch it in midair and make off. He could not capture fish himself as once in the water he would have been unable to rise again on wet wings. So for years the ospreys had supplied his fish diet.

One day during the fourth week of Ed's stay on the lake he chanced to be watching Whitehead indulge in his favorite sport. For an hour the old bird had brooded on a snag with his keen eyes fixed on a fishing osprey. Ed did not know it but the eagle was especially hungry. For two days he had been unsuccessful in hunting and now was determined to break his fast with fish. Suddenly the osprey dived and came up with a large sucker in his talons. Not allowing the hawk to get as high as was his custom Whitehead swung after him. For once he was too eager. The osprey dropped the fish when but a scant hundred feet above the water and forgetting caution in his hunger the robber dropped like a plummet after it. As the fish neared the water he was almost upon it and with the food so close forgot his fear of water. He struck the water with force enough to drive him under and came up with every feather soaked. His wet wings refused to raise his heavy body from the water. His struggles beat foam on the surface and sent the waves rolling toward the shores.

Coran did not refuse the aid the gods offered. He was in his canoe and paddling rapidly toward the eagle before he had been in the water a minute. As he came near, Old Whitehead, worn out with his struggling, lay quietly upon the surface and did not even offer a protest as Ed leaned over and slipped a sack over him and lifted him into the canoe.

Back at camp, Coran constructed a pen of wooden bars and

placed the bedraggled bird inside. There he drooped, wet and half drowned, recovering his strength. Ed went about packing his camp equipment in preparation for the trip to the city, and suddenly he found himself regretting that the time had come for him to leave. He just now realized how much he had come to love the place and to feel himself a part of it. As a fond farewell he started out to walk around the lake.

While Ed was gone the warm sun shone down upon the cage and quickly brought new life to Old Whitehead. As his feathers dried the old strength flowed back into his body and the old fire burned in his savage eyes. He fought the bars like a demon, but to no avail. Very soon he realized the futility of such effort and became quiet as one does when engaged in deep thought.

When Ed returned there was a pensive, half sad expression in his eyes. The very thought of leaving was hateful. Something seemed to be pulling at him, drawing him back. For a moment he allowed the picture of himself back in the city to dwell in his mind. Then he straightened his shoulders and snapped his fingers with an air of finality.

"I'll come back here," he said, "and stay. I'll build a shack and be a trapper and guide. Yes, sir, just as soon as I take that bird to the zoo I'll come back."

With this happy thought he went to the cage and looked long at Old Whitehead. The eagle stood now in all his proud beauty as though in silent contempt of his captor. Coran looked closer. Truly, he was a magnificent bird. From his talons to his hooked beak he was every inch the king of birds. From his eyes there flashed a gleam of wildness; a gleam that is seen only in the eyes of those of God's creatures that are forever free and love freedom above all else. In a free animal it is a beautiful, savage gleam; in a captive it is a sight to wring the heart.

Whitehead moved across behind the bars and suddenly Ed seemed to become aware of their presence between himself and the bird. A flashing vision struck him. He saw himself behind iron bars with that same wild gleam in his eyes. The vision changed. He saw the great Whitehead behind the iron bars of a zoo with a staring crowd in front. He envisioned that flashing eye growing dull and sullen as the proud spirit bowed and the savage eagle heart broke, pining for the freedom it once had known.

There was a twitching about his mouth and a strange wetness

126

on his lashes as Ed bent down, with a peculiar softness, and opened the door of the cage. Old Whitehead stepped forth with the slow dignity of a regal king and stood for a moment in silent pride before his mighty wings beat the air and he soared aloft to rule once more as king of the upper air.

****

CINDERELLA UP-TO-DATE

A ghostly silence held sway over the old college dormitory. A silence that was only broken by the occasional maniacal shriek of a mouse between the walls or the groan of an expiring freshman who took studies seriously. The atmosphere was that of a medieval torture dungeon.

In her tiny room Cinderella sat among the littered books and papers and cried copiously. Tears the size of an ordinary egg dropped from her great hazel eyes with mechanical regularity and splashed into the pool at her feet. Cinderella did not even remove her already wet feet from the vicinity of the deepening pool, for it was Saturday night anyhow.

Saturday was what caused all the trouble. Now the trouble was not that Cinderella disliked the ancient custom of the Saturday night bath, nor was it the fact that she must study her Sunday school lesson for tomorrow. Cinderella was a very proper little girl and took her bath almost every week and went to Sunday school every time the class had a picnic. The difficulty with this Saturday was that it was the date of the big reception in honor of Cecil Howard, the great flying hero.

When the old college honored a hero, it did the job up right. Everything was complete from soup to dog biscuits. All arrangements had been made even to the exclusion of freshmen. And that was why Cinderella appeared to have entered the latest weeping marathon, for she was a freshman.

Suddenly Cinderella noticed a great fly struggling in the pool of her production and being of a nature that could not stand anything more cruel than poisoning orphans or drowning little chickens she stooped and flipped the hapless insect out of the salty brine. Instantly the fly shook itself like an ancient Ford and stood transformed in the form of a queer old lady, who as

127

Cinderella gaped at her with an astonishment that denoted adenoids, spoke, "Why do you bawl, Cinderella?"

"O, Grandmother, I am a freshie and can't go to the hop," replied Cinderella, for she knew it must be her grandmother since the old lady so closely resembled the creature so often spoken of in connection with Darwin's theory.

"That's easy," replied the old lady. "Powder your nose and swipe your roommate's dress while I make other arrangements."

In nothing flat Cinderella was ready and slid down the fire escape in answer to a hail from the street. There stood a handsome spring wagon with six juniors hitched in the traces. Cinderella could hardly control her exultation when she saw that the six were those most prominent in the enforcement of freshman rules. The stuffy old footman was none other than her most hated English teacher and the driver the president of the student body. All seemed in a stupor, for Grandma had given each a shot from her hip flask.

The obsequious footman assisted her into the carriage and closed the door. "Drive like hell or you get hell," she snapped to the driver and they were off.

"Remember to leave before 6 A.M.," called Grandma, "or the charm is off."

At the door of the hall Cinderella left orders for the six juniors to be tied closely to the hitching rack and to be given neither food or drink. She locked the carriage doors and ordered the footman and driver to stand at attention on the outside, for it was raining pitchforks.

At the dance our heroine was a wow. No one knew her and many were the inquiries as to her identity. Her beauty was so entrancing that not one of the boys noticed that she was a terrible dancer or that she danced more on her partner's feet than her own.

About four in the morning when the dance was getting well started and the first drunk had just begun to dance on a table, Cecil Howard noticed our heroine. If she had not fallen in a heap he probably would not have seen her, but now that he had been forced to observe her he could not take his eyes from her face. Consequently he never noticed the immense size of her feet or the genuine Chippewa shoes she wore.

By five they had fought out six dances and sat out a dozen. The whole crowd was gossiping and the Female Anvil Chorus had condemned Cinderella to banishment while the male population had devised many and torturous forms of death for one Cecil Howard. But all things must have an end, even lectures sometimes end. Right in the middle of a dreamy waltz the clock struck six. The charm vanished. Snatched away was the beautiful dress belonging to one outraged roommate and Cinderella stood in the center of the floor clothed in an underwear effect that her dear old aunt Matilda had made from flour sacks. Across a prominent part of her anatomy was written in black face type "Pillsbury's Best."

Cecil gasped and everybody else shrieked. With a wild howl Cinderella stepped on the gas and left at ninety per. At the door one of her shoes, no longer able to keep the pace, came off. When a frantic search revealed no trace of the missing belle, Cecil returned to the ballroom. There he was informed by a servant that the lady had lost one of her gondolas as she departed.

"Find the girl who can wear it and I'll marry her," he said.

Eight girls were killed in the rush to try on the shoe but none could wear it. It was too large for even the largest of feet. At last the messenger reached the dormitory. There even the flat-footed matron could not fill the enormous cavity. When the messenger arrived at Cinderella's room she came to he door wearing one shoe and a carpet slipper. The messenger took one look at her feet and shouted, "I've got her."

They were married next day and left for Niagara Falls. They lived happily ever after and all their children are famous for their big feet.

THE PLANTER

On sun drenched hill I dug a space
Of warm moist native soil.
A youthful tree I carried there
To plant with carefree toil.

I spread the roots with prudent love
And tucked them in with care.
With my two feet I packed the earth
About my seedling rare.

So now today when distance calls
I vision places fair,
But know for certain that I placed
My own life roots up there.

Tree planting 1967.

LETTER TO THE EDITOR

Since writing things in prose,
I haven't made a dime
It has just occurred to me
To try my hand at rhyme.

Now if you'll just glance over
My dialetic verse
I think that you'll agree
You've printed things much worse.

Perhaps some sober hunters
Or campers rough and hale
Might like to read the verses
That tell this hunting tale.

Of course if you reject it,
I'll not bite the bit and champ
And just for sake of safety
I'll enclose the usual stamp.

RAINBOW'S END

I went today to mend the pasture fence
April laughed at me in my old worn coat
Her laugh was so tinkling I took no offense
Somehow I felt and shared her lilting note.

Here was a place my fence crossed the brook,
Now it is torn away by heavy spring flows,
The little brook chuckled at my frowning look
Then slipped over the stones to hide in the willows.

I waded through the saucy little vandal
To gather up my broken wire strand
(So barbed and tangled it's hard to handle)
And on the other side was marshy land.

136

A little pool not more than four feet wide
Smiled at me with proud and happy face
How foolish for a whole blue sky to hide
In shallow depth of such a little space.

Beside the pool on some forgotten day
A rainbow surely rested upon the swampy mould.
And then in wild retreat from the sun's bright ray
Forgot to take away the magic heap of gold.

With green velvet carpet setting off its color bright
Flaunting beauty, matchless glory and a wealth untold,
With a loveliness entrancing to humble sight
Stood a single blazing clump of marsh marigold.

LIFE'S PATHWAY

I'm travelling today down a lovely lane
Through a land that the fairies have made.
Its beauty is woven with trees and moss
And flowers that can not fade.

I know as I walk this radiant path
Where loveliness can not wane,
That never again so long as life lasts
May I pass this way again.

So I must harken to every sound
And garner each glowing sight,
I must touch each flower, embrace each breeze
And bathe in this crystalline light.

Before I come to the end of the lane,
I'll plant one flower so fair
That others who journey along with me
Will know that I've been there.

And when I get to the end of the way,
I'll turn for a last long look
And fix each beautiful thing that's there
On a page in my memory book.

137

THE MEASURE OF GREATNESS

What is the measure of a great man?
Is it the house in which he dwells?
Is it the kind of car he drives,
Or the wealth of which he tells?

These are but empty honors
The man who is great you will find,
Is the one who is of most service
And holds the regard of mankind.

If the nation's mourn your passing
Though your farewell be early or late,
If men feel a loss at your leaving,
Then you've been truly great.

LIFE'S COST

I have but reached that age
Which men call prime
But the calendar of human things
Differs from the reckonings of Time.

Time counts not the wax candles we gain,
But the many things we have lost.
He takes of my treasures, one by one,
I audit them all to life's cost.

Carefree childhood the years took in fee,
Youth's pleasures rendered vain.
Man's dominating tasks impoored,
Recorded sorrow on the brain.

Hopes and ambitions now dimly glow
The zest of life begins to fade,
My face with its lines is a signed receipt
That the toll of years is paid.

DREAMS

I hitched my carriage to the steeds
Whose manes were billowed fire
On burnished hoofs they spurned the earth:
We sailed above the mire.

Triumphant in the driver's seat
While years unnoted fled
I bowled among the glowing stars
And scorned the thunder head.

And now I'm dropping back to earth
My steeds are worn and tired.
My dreams no longer hold me up
And oh 'tis hard, 'tis hard.

IF I SHOULD DIE TONIGHT

If I should die tonight
I must not bemoan my lot
For I have lived and tasted life.
I know the beauty of the dawn,
I've heard the song of birds,
Nature's beauty shone for me
In flower, tree and teeming sod.
I know the night of million stars
I've walked in hand with God.

TWILIGHT CALL

Thickening twilight o'er village street heralds the close of day,
Shadows pulse with happy sound of children at their play.
The evening star peeps shyly from Heaven's vast blue dome
Clear and sweet a mother's voice calls her children home.

Darkening shadows over my life come with the added years,
The blackness throbs expectantly to a thousand nameless fears.
Listening intently I pray to hear out from Heaven's dome
Calm and sweet a Father's voice calling His children home.

AN EVENING PRAYER

Dear Lord, I'm grateful for this day.
I've watched the wild things at their play,
I've fished a brawling mountain brook,
Accept my thanks, I pray.

With strength to take me where I go;
With eyes to see and mind to know;
Your world is mine. I'm grateful, Lord!
Please keep me always so.

THANK YOU, GOD

For all the march of days has done,
For season's rain and ripening sun,
For life and health, for hope eternal;
For wealth of years and joys diurnal,
For valued friend and priceless love,
We offer thanks to God above.

POSSESSIONS

The pompous owner said
    "My slave."
The slave replied
    "My Master."

Bitter grief attended one;
Quiet sleep the other.
The placid slave remarked
    "My slave?"
The owner said
    "Yes, Master."

I SEE! I SEE!

Blind Bartimeus sought our Lord
And begged the gift of sight.
And to his long-darkened eyes
There came the blessed light.
How wonderful if He would come
And touch both you and me,
That both of us could truly say,
At last, I see! I see!

THE PULSE OF GOD

Long ages past, I fled a jangled world:
Heard its snarling hatred fade behind me.
From misty eons I've returned, a new creation.
I lived with ageless things; parcel of eternity.
I have shared with patriarchs, Plato, Paul and Moses.
I picked an acorn from the earth
And held life in my hand.

Over misty hills I saw the sun arise.
I tasted the tangy strawberry of the wild:
I heard the symphony of a waterfall.
And the chorus of frogs at twilight.
I stretched my length on teeming sod.
I laid my cheek against a shaggy spruce
And sensed the pulse of God.

THE MASTER'S CALL

In a long forgotten village
There spread a rumor great
That the Lord would pay a visit
On a certain foretold date.

As the time approached, each household
With preparations fair,
Began to hope the Master
Would make his visit there.

The rich man set a table
With all good foods aright.
The priest prepared an altar
With candles flaming bright.

A woman decked her doorway
With welcome signs aglow,
And scrubbed her guest room
To house the Lord, you know.

The banker placed his money
To be at his command.
The farmer planned to show him
His great expanse of land.

Old Caleb had not known
About the Master's call,
The townsmen had not bothered
To let him know at all.

The Lord had come so sudden
And found him on the street
Removing broken glass
Lest some child might cut its feet.

ALONE

Alone at darkest midnight hour
I look on Galilee strand
While others sleep I restless roam
There's blood upon my hand.

Alone! My feet rouse echoes in
Strange streets of alien lands.
I'm driven on with soul storm tossed
By blood upon my hands.

Alone! I walk the garden cold
A cock crow breaks night bands,
The dew wet branch can't wash away
That blood from off my hands.

Alone! by night's accusing stars
I seek the seabeach sands,
In vain! the ocean will not take
The blood that's on my hands.

Alone! I rule the throngs no more!
Alone! I bear Cain's brand!
Alone! I'll stand at Judgement bar!
With blood upon my hand.

THE FANATIC

He raises pious hands to a distant God on high
His gleaming eye is fixed on distant sky
With straining heart he drives on to his goal
Nor turns to right or left along his road.
Thus blinded by the white heat of his goodness
He spurns mankind from his path with hurrying feet
And tramples others under straining feet.

143

GOD'S MIRROR

A little star in the heavenly night
Scrubbed and polished with all her might.
She burnished her face and gilded her points
God smiled and said, "How bright you look."

Another star gathered dirt and soot
And scattered it over her sisters there.
"Now," thought she, "mid their darkened faces
Mine will shine bright beyond compare."
God said, "You look unusually dull tonight."

BROKEN DREAMS

I once lived in a lovely house
Whose walls iridescent gleam
Reflected such light of rainbow hue
As are found in a fairyland dream.

Through fragile halls there floated a haze
Filled with bubbles so flashing and rare
'Twas a pleasure celestial there to dwell
In a dazed enchantment fair.

Years battered down the delicate walls;
Broke the bubbles all one by one
I live my days now in a soiled house
Whose walls are dull, rough stone.

ACROSS THE PAST

Backward I look across a trail rough and long
Where cold winds bite and whine a dismal song.
Close set, distorted—ugly milestones of years
Gloat as sated vultures on the pathway splotched with tears.

Beyond the forlorn vista in a rose tinted nook
You move ever from me with sad parting look.
My head bows in sorrow; I know I can not win
Across the Past between me and the life that might have been.

THIS PLACE WAS ONCE A HOME

Just an old lone chimney
Of stones so true and square,
Firmly set to tell us
Of life that prospered there.

Beyond it broken fences
Of old and rotting rails
Mark off the steep sloped pastures
From cultivated vales.

A stubborn ancient lilac,
Gnarled roots deep in the loam,
Sighs sadly to the passing breeze
"This place was once a home."

CONFLICT

Through idyllic days of summer
In the kingdom of the stream
There arose a sleepy murmur
Like the whispers of a dream.

Every creature of the kingdom
Shared alike the happy lot,
Went his way in peace and sunshine,
Never dreamed of traitor's plot.

Till there came a sorry morning
When a tyrant through surprise
Caught the happy kingdom napping,
Bound it close with winter's ties.

There was heard no cheerful murmur,
Song of bird or drone of bee,
Not a flower glowed or whitened
For the searcher's eye to see.

Sorry, stricken lay the kingdom
Neath the conqueror's iron might
Deeply buried all its pleasure
Under coat of deathly white.

But the tyrant proud and haughty
Failed to note that under ground,
There still remained an army
Yet unseen and never bound.

And now there comes a murmur,
Growing ominous day by day,
Of the mighty forces gathering
To end the monarch's sway.

Through rupture in the snow sheet
Muddy rivulets now creep.
Kakai troops in number mustering
Down the hillside rush and leap.

146

Now the mighty armies gather
Sun, Birds, Flowers forces bring.
Winter flees the battle beaten
Hail its conqueror, Sweet Spring!

(Last verse by Eugene Burner)

MOTHER NATURE

Oh, Mother Nature, skilled musician
With your organ many keyed;
Teach us we pray your rhythm,
Make our ears your music heed.

May we see your dawn tipped fingers
O'er the sounding keyboard stray;
May our souls drink in your glory
Of the prelude to the day.

Teach us with your timeless wisdom
Hidden notes that years have lain
Unheard among the noises,
In the drumming of the rain.

Let our souls be not mistrusting
When the dark cloud clothes your form,
Rather hear with reverent feeling
The wild crescendo of the storm.

I NEED TO GO TO THE WOODS

I need to go to the woods today,
(I am sick at soul of the human way).
I need to touch old massive trees,
I need the embrace of a fleeting breeze.

I need to know the feel of the moss,
(I am weary of trade and gain and loss).
I need to hear the dropping acorn,
I need to see the dawn newborn.

I need to come home on a winding trail,
(Knowing now that God will not fail).
I need to see nature going to rest,
I need to feel that all's for the best.

NIOBE*

Etched pale against a wintry sky
"The spreading chestnut stands";
Sad marker of a race now gone
She glooms above our land.

Her seed once fed the forest life;
She cast them free as rain;
Her offspring clothed the sloping hill
And cooled the pleasant lane.

Lone mother of a countless horde,
With naked arms wide spread,
She yearns above the whitened forms
Of children stark and dead.

   *Niobe was a Greek mother who lost all her
children as punishment by the Gods.

RAMBLING

A dozen trails laced through a wood
A score of signs said come.
With enamored eyes I looked at the paths.
I wanted to follow them all.

I played hopscotch over the maze
With a foot in one or the other.
I played the game of crazy jumps
Till evening shadows came.

Then I discovered to my surprise
I had reached the end of none.

I WANT TO KNOW

I want to know the bird that sings.
I want to know each flower that springs.
I want to know the beaver's way.
I want to know what wise men say.

I want to know the bird that sings.
The tree that sways to the breeze,
The insect low that chirps his note,
All things—
For then they are truly mine.

DESTINY

Heralded from afar with ominous roar
The flying gale drives through the autumn wood.
Great oaks bow their kingly crowns in fear:
Suppliant weeds kiss the forest floor.

Straining branches lashing in awful pain
Release a flying tumult of frostbitten leaves,
Brown, red and yellow in blinding swarm
To strike the earth as thickly as showered rain.

In the solemn calm that follows the storm
A huge yellow leaf quietly parts its grasp
And floats gently down to rest.

THE SPIRIT OF FALL

As a cautious urchin stows away
His binding Sunday clothes
And glides away as a furtive ghost
To the haymow's joyous repose.

So I today tucked away my cares
In corners out of sight,
And stole away to the deep old woods
Resplendent in Autumn's light.

The joy of a youngster in my heart
And his lightness in my feet,
While I heard the scurry of busy life;
Felt the pulse of the outdoors beat.

I gazed in awe at the festive trees
Clothed in carnival attire.
Heard them rustle and saw them sway
Serving Gypsy Wind as a lyre.

150

Rushing hither and scurrying yon
The plume-tailed gray squirrel went,
Barking and sneezing like idle folk
On gossip's mischief bent.

With raucous whoops a flock of jays
Tortured a staid old owl
To rebuke him well for his sour face
Mongst bright and happy fowl.

Down in a hollow a tiny brook
Had caught the spirit of fall,
And decked her face with brilliant leaves
Filched from the trees so tall.

I felt the wood reach out as a friend
To take me to its heart.
And I thrilled to know in the grand display
I had just a tiny part.

On the journey home in the failing light
When the rays of the sun were spent,
My soul seemed filled from the woodland spring
With a measureless great content.

Now would you believe that back at home
When I reached for my burden of care,
In spite of the diligence of my search
I couldn't find it there.

DROUTH

The summer has died too soon.
Drouth wove her dusty pall.
The verdant promise of her spring
Is dead beyond recall.

The sun is a molten ball of brass
It scorches the dry cracked clay.
Shimmering heat goes up in waves
From the desolate highway.

Bawling cattle stir the dust.
They starve on pasture slopes.
Heartsick, the farmer turns his face
From fields of blasted hopes.

The creek has long ceased to flow.
Its bed is bleached white stones,
They sprawl along the valley,
Like long-dead serpent bones.

The garden is lone and neglected
The flower bears no seed.
Like grieving Hebrew virgin,
She droops near the withered weed.

The weed and flower are sisters.
Their beauty and strength are lost
They await in kinship of sorrow
The pitying stroke of the frost.

THE GREAT HORNED OWL

Far from the lonely ridges
Rolling through night's black pall
Eerie and sad, hollow, haunting
I hear the hoot owl call.

"Witches moving," cry the children.
"Bad weather," the rustic sage.
"Hard winter," groans the prophet.
"Sign of death," croaks withered age.

But I stand in the darkened valley
And hark to his lonely call
As his solemn bass rolls downward
Out from the ridges tall.

I do not call him prophet,
Thing of evil, sage or seer.
He's a part of the mystic night-time
And his voice I love to hear.

CHRISTMAS GREETINGS

In the calm of Christmas evening,
Curled within my easy chair,
I sorted through the greeting cards
And read each message there.

Just the usual season's wishes
From the corners of the earth,
And the stereotyped phrases
That recall the Saviour's birth.

But behind each printed folder
From the rich or from the poor,
My mind could see the welcome
Of a friendly open door.

And between each line of greeting
Such to make the teardrops start,
Was the ever-warming image
Of an overflowing heart.

MEMORIES

Last night, Dear, a soft film of mist
Tangled the moon's bright beam.
The voice of darkness fell to low cadence
As you stole into my dream.

The air was incensed with your fragrance
Troops of memories around me milled.
You touched my cheek; nestled in my arms
And an aching void was filled.

The curtain of years rolled backward,
The bliss of our meeting seemed
The dearest sort of reality;
Years between us, the part I had dreamed.

TONIGHT

Tonight, I'll clasp your hand in mine
Perhaps I'll hold it tight
It's just because we're happy
And our hearts are gay and light.

Tonight, I'll bid you fond farewell
Perchance my voice will break.
There's sure to be some little thing
To make old memory wake.

Tonight, a dampness clouds our eyes
As the final tableau nears
We'll both pretend it's only mist
We're just too gay for tears.

TO MY WIFE

Many days have slipped away
Since you and I were one,
Days of sunlight and of shadow
Days of toil and days of fun.

And as each speeding hour
Flits away on fleeting wing,
I think how much you mean to me,
How much of joy you bring.

The fret and care of daily strife,
Your smile can drive away.
In face of flight producing odds,
Your courage bids me stay.

When friendships old begin to fail,
When appears no helping hand,
I turn to find you at my side
To help, to cheer and understand.

Thus with me you'll share the load,
The path you'll brighten with your smile;
Comes the storm or comes the sunshine
Till we've travelled life's last mile.

ADVICE TO A BRIDEGROOM

Don't say we didn't warn you
Of your horrible, awful fate!
We told you not to do it
Before it was too late.

She'll beat you and she'll bang you
She'll make of you a wreck.
She'll spend your dough, pull out your hair
And darn near break your neck.

155

Your days of joy are over
Your happy hours are done
Life holds for you just labor
And very little fun.

You've made the great and awful leap
As a million fools have done,
But you have this consolation
You're not in the boat alone.

May God ease your pains
Bring balm for your sorrows
And give you some hope
Of better tomorrows.

WALLS

Walls between Neighbors
Walls between Nations
We are unconscious builders of Walls.

Hatred toward Neighbors
Hatred toward Nations
Hatred thrives best behind a strong Wall.

Love between Neighbors
Love between Nations
Love can not scale impregnable Walls.

Christ among Neighbors
Christ above Nations
Christ's love can level impregnable Walls.

A SCRAPBOOK

Quiet, mute, I speak with a hundred tongues
Unmoving, lifeless, I breathe with undying lungs
Unmindful of events, yet historian of the ages
Unschooled, untaught, I teach the wisdom of ages
Taciturn, impassive, I move to tears or smiles
For I keep cherished memories recorded in my files
Fed with scraps of wit, wisdom or immortal verse
Clothed only in patches, I am the beauty of the universe.

CROWDED OUT

No, lady, I don't deny it
Your statement's as true as they come.
I'm not in ill health or down on my luck
In plain language I'm just an old bum.

I like to be honest; make no pretense
One virtue still clings to my name.
Most I once had, are hopelessly lost
And my life's but a record of shame.

But I'd like to tell you in words that are true
That I haven't always been so,
I once was respected and lived in a house
Where we spat at the name of "hobo."

I've seen "both sides of the track" in my time,
I lived on a smug little street,
With a wife and two kids in a neat little home
That we nicknamed "Peaceful Retreat."

And I thought I was blest above all men
In the love of my handsome wife.
Hers was a love I thought would stay
Linked with mine to the end of our life.

157

But what's the use to tire you out
With a story that's always so old.
You know the climax: everyone does.
The love of my loved one grew cold.

No, she didn't elope with "the other man"
Nor seek a divorce in the court,
But surrounded herself with a hundred things
That left no room for my sort.

Time for parties, time for church,
For the children, for clubs and for tea,
Time for charity, time for her cats,
But no space of time for me.

My story's not new there are millions more
Of men, like me, about
Whom the neighbors think are happy and blest
But *they* know they've been crowded out.

You know how it goes from here on through.
I longed for companionship sweet.
I found the best that I could right then
Drink, and women of the street.

So I drifted of course from bad to worse
Scarcely knowing the end to come.
And here I am at the end of my rope,
You're right, lady, just an old bum.

LIFE'S TREADMILL

Hurry, man, hurry
Work around the sun.
With lodge, club, convention
You must run, run, run.

LAZY LITTLE ROAD

Lazy Little Road! Ah's a talkin' to you.
Now you perk right up and heah me through.
No use you tryin' to glide away,
An hide wheah you can't heah what I say.
Lazy Little Road!

Ah sees you makin' yoself a lane
'Twixt dem fields of wavin' grain.
Ah knows you'se gwine to slip away
Through dat patch of new mowed hay.
Lazy Little Road!

Look at you now! You thinks dat brook
Gwine to make you a hidin' nook.
No! Wuss'n dat! You, lazy as sin!
You thinks a brook's to waller in!
Lazy Little Road!

Don' tell me now you's gonna mock
Good roads, a curlin' roun' dat mossy rock!
You means you loves dem tamaracks?
You likes de flowers atween de tracks?
Lazy Little Road!

Hah! Ah sees de curlin' loops
You makes aroun' dem cottage stoops.
Ah guess you likes dem homey folks·
And dat is why so slow you pokes.
Lazy Little Road!

Don' you see dem trees you love
Is closin' you in from de sky above?
Don' you know dey'll kiver you deep
When Autumn leaves come down to sleep?
Lazy Little Road!

Ain't you shamed when lovers stroll,
And ketch de moon where you tops de knoll?
Don' you wish you could lead 'em straight?
Your lazy ways keeps 'em out late!
Lazy Little Road!

You's a lover yourself. You hugs de trees.
You loves de flowers and honey bees.
You sweet talks folks dat come your way
And make de stranger want to stay.
Lazy Little Road!

Look ovah deah at de big turnpike.
Now deah's a road dat's sumpin' like!
It bridge de ribber and lebel de hills;
It bury de brook, and de valley it fills;
Busy Turnpike!

You take a lesson you lazy road!
Dat turnpike's packin' a mighty load.
And you loaf 'round and dwadle heah,
Wid de changin' show of de livelong yeah.
Lazy Little Road!

Ah sees you smirk and glide away.
De folks all love you, so they say.
It res dere souls to tramp on you.
Lazy Road! Ah loves you too.
Lazy Little Road!

"DOING WHAT COMES NATURALLY"

I'll tell ye, Doc, it's funny. Seems there's two sides ter see.
Reckon though I'm wrong. Most generally that's what I be.
I hear it on the radio and read it in the news.
And now I've had a lecture of your medical views.
It appears if I drink my water from a spring or hand dug well,
I'll catch my death of microbes as sure as fire in hell.
If I drink raw milk, I'm a goner. Fever will get me sure.
Can't touch a unpeeled apple. The dang thing just ain't pure.

160

By smokin' I'll get lung cancer and kick off quicker'n scat.
With a trip in an autymobile I'm bumped off just like that.
When I grab a gun and go huntin', I'm temptin' fate that's all
Some lug is sure to get me with a soft nosed rifle ball.
I got to get my check up, my shots and vaccine too
If my bed ain't fumigated, the durn thing just won't do.
I have to strain the air I breathe and stay out of a breeze,
Cause every other week or so you find a new disease.
I get a little ailment that makes some doctor sick.
He says it is an allergy an' I thought I had the itch.
I get so durn discouraged that I am just about
To let 'em call for Finley to come and lay me out.
But then there was my grandfolks, old timers dumb as hogs,
Who wintered in the breezes that whistled through the logs.
They smoked home spun and chawed it in very careless ways
They spat the juice in sawdust and left it there for days.
They drank from jug or bottle, cow track, stream or ditch.
And if they got an allergy, they scratched and called it itch.
They ate ground hog with gusto, munched apples where they
    growed.
And wouldn't a knowed a microbe if they met one in the road.
They never heerd o' vaccine or had a saving "shot"
They lived and loved and laughed and died to be buried on the
    spot.
Funny though, at eighty, those dumb clucks are still alive
But, Doc, you'll work yourself to death before you're sixty-five.

NICK'S COON HUNT

Now leesten meester salesman,
I com to buy fur coat.
I no care eef eet cheepmunk
Or maybe beely goat.

De buttons she don't matter,
De style he ees de same.
You sell me coat from monkey
Or ape weeth deeferent name.

161

You no catch my trouble?
You theenk me maybe notts?
You wait I tal you story
Bout me weeth houn dog mutts.

My wife Angela tal me.
Weeth feest right by my nose
"Ees coming oop soon Chreesmas,
You get for me fur clothes."

I tal you she ees scare me
When she mak dat kind of sound.
She got wan hellish temper
And she weigh tree hondred pound.

Bot queek like flash wan idee
Gat een my head right soon.
I buy for me wan beeg houn dog
And go to hunt for coon.

"Now see," I tell Angela,
"You dressing mighty soon
Weeth neckpiece make from possum
Weeth overcoat from coon."

I send way out een country
And buy me wan beeg houn.
He look like drayman's skeeny horse
Eat evertheeng een town.

I say to my freend Tony,
"Thees night ees much beeg moon;
You want much fun, you com along
We go for geet some coon."

We ride much out een country.
That road he ees so bad
My houn dog seet een hind seat
And howl like he gone mad.

Een woods by great beeg cornfield
We loose dog off from chain.
Five meenutes by my wan bock watch
He howl like he got pain.

Much queek we run toward houn dog;
I theenk we got not sense.
We step een swamp; bomp eento tree
Wrap op een barb-wire fence.

We tear my pants; we reep hees shirt
We lose one yard of skeen.
We run again: we bump een log
And beat op all four shin.

Wan limb reach out and catch me
With wallop under cheen;
My feet fly op my head go down.
And out go all my weend.

Bot I so tough, I betcha;
Som time I gat to tree,
Where houn dog set and bark like fool
At sometheeng we don't see.

Eet ees so dark een pine tree,
Weethout much light from moon,
We no can see no reeng tail
Bot we theenk we tree beeg coon.

Weeth flashlight in hind pocket
I start to climb op tree;
I lose my hat, I bump my head,
Knock skin off both my knee.

Eet take me most wan hour
Till I get up een high place
I flash my light; I almost die
At what looks me een face.

163

My heart she jomp eento my neck;
My breath ees almost fail;
That coon like giant pussy cat
Weeth leetle stubby tail.

Hees eyes they are so yellow,
Hees teeth they look so sharp,
I'm theenk about Saint Peter
And playing on my harp.

Down far below yell Tony,
"Why not you shake heem down
He no can get away, I theenk,
From me and thees big houn."

I got no need for shaking leemb;
I'm shaking just like jelly;
I fall off limb; land on my back
And coon land on my belly.

Queek like a flash he rushes een,
That gol blame, dam fool houn.
He meeses coon gets hold on me
Een place where I seet down.

I'm holding coon by one hind leg;
He makes from me a wreck.
Tony grabs op heavy club
Heets me in back of neck.

I make da grab for big black rock,
For bop coon over ear.
My hand seenk een; ees mucha soft;
I guess som cows com here.

That coon he bite me on my hand;
Hees feet make reebons of me.
I turn heem loose; give wan beeg jump
And I go op een tree.

My houn ees run like devil com.
Tony ees hide like rat.
I'm seein' now when he walk off
That coon ees wildcat.

So sell me now wan fur coat
Possum, skunk or mushy rat.
For when Angela ees gat mad
She worse than wildcat.

GENERATION GAP

In days of old our parents bold
Brought forth a little legion
Cute hellions dear; one new each year
Would populate the region.
The doctor bold or a midwife old
Spanked each a healthy whack
Washed him in soap without any dope
And rolled him in a gunny sack.
In a cast off shirt, not so free from dirt
He was dressed from neck to tail
And ready in advance, his three cornered pants
Were pinned with a ten penny nail.
By yells and squeals he ordered his meals
That came from nature's store.
For vitamins hale he chewed the cat's tail
Or stole the dog's lunch from the floor.
He grew like a weed on his crude brand of feed
And ate what he chanced to like
He swallowed whole germs and likely some worms
Then cut teeth on a railroad spike.
The years went by and time drew nigh
To the start of his few school days
Where they straightened him out with a hickory sprout
When he fell into crooked ways.
Days went past and came at last
The time of great elation.
When father sighed and mother cried
At grade school graduation.

In days so new with kids so few
We use quite modern customs
We look with hate on long past dates
And most sincerely cuss 'em.
With much eclat the modern brat
Is born in his father's pain.
Pre-publicized, deodorized
And wrapped in cellophane.
He starts that day in a Spartan way
On a system most amazing.
He's vaccinated, fumigated
And other things quite crazing.
He's powdered and oiled, his playthings boiled
At a thousand odd degrees
While pop throws a fit; mom cries a bit
If the little dear should sneeze.
They study the book with serious look
That tells how kids are reared.
And to his needs the household deeds
And all its acts are geared.
His food is tested; predigested;
Carefully formulized,
Plain milk is banned; it must be canned
And surely pasteurized.
His clothes are boiled, his chassis oiled
Just as the book dictates.
At the clinic he's weighed; his growth surveyed
At regular two week dates
To the specialist carted, he's graphed and charted
And his I.Q. is carefully made.
His traits are uncovered; reflexes discovered
And his brain to the ounce is weighed.
At six comes the day, in time's usual way
When he ushered into school
And pop explains those super brains
To a teacher he thinks is a fool.
He must have his way from day to day
Or he'll develop foul neuroses
He's a sensitive male; don't paddle his tail
Or you'll give him inhibitions.

Correction's a bane; just give him full rein
To follow his natural urge.
If he rolls in the mire; sets the schoolhouse afire
It's just an innocent splurge.

But again at last, time moving fast
Brings the day of great elation
When father sighs and mother cries
At reform school graduation.

THE POLITICIAN

Now listen to me neighbors, I'm here to tell you plain
I ain't no politician what's out for worldly gain
I ask it as a favor of you, my dearest friends
To help me beat that feller what's out for his own ends.
He's a liar and a horse thief with a solid ivory dome
And he's the crooked so and so that burnt the orphan's home.
When he was just a youngun in some town or other,
He stole and sold the spectacles of his own dear old mother.
He's out lied Ananias and out robbed Jesse James,
He's master of the double cross and other sinful games.
His father was a pig thief and his mother was a hag
His brothers all is convicts and his sister an old bag.
He went to church one Sunday, cain't remember when,
Put a dollar in the collection and sneaked out ten.
He claims he's edjacated, with larnin' nuff to spare
But he only went to school three days and the teacher wasn't
    there.
About his days of honest toil he's tellin' all you chaps
But he got them blisters on his hands from shootin' crooked
    craps.
Yes sir, boys, he's lousy; he's a stinker and a bum
He's a lazy good for nothing and he's jest plain dumb.
His lies and awful stories is the worst kind o' bunk
Fer he couldn't mingle social-like with a self respectin' skunk.
He's the joke of all the humans, jest a out and out dud
But I won't talk about him cause I don't sling mud.
I'm only here to tell you what a break it would be
Fer this whole country if you'd jest elect me.

I been sober, sane and honest since the tender age of four
And I've read the Bible fifty times and maybe twenty more.
I've helped the sick and fed the poor and dried the orphan's
tears.
I never drunk no liquor nor touched a drop of beer.
I'm loyal to my church, my country and my town,
I'm as lowly and as humble as a Blue tick hound.
I don't want the job fer money and I don't want fame
I jest want to serve my country and glorify her name.
I'll improve your roads and harbors and build you better
schools
I'll set the country hummin' to a dozen golden rules.
Your friends will be promoted and your enemies be shot
And there'll be a dozen chickens fer every cookin' pot.
Your taxes will be lowered or else eliminated
The good will be uplifted and the bad be truly hated.
I'll give you all a ticket to Saint Peter's gate
And if you shouldn't make it, there'll be a cash rebate.
Now even my opponent or any fool can see
That the man to be elected is no other one but me.
You know if I am chosen, I'll serve the country well
And if I'm not elected, you can all go to hell.

So "it" was
when life began

Originally printed in

West Virginia Hillbilly

Richwood, W. Va.

SNAKES

Bobby Burns believed in giving breaks, why shouldn't I? He
wrote a poem in honor of a louse and one to the devil, so I'll

175

give a few lines to debunking a lot of nasty fibs on the gent who started a lot of trouble in the Garden of Eden. I mean the belly crawling chaps known as snakes.

When we have an inborn fear of anything we are inclined to do a little truth stretching when we talk about him. As a result all bears are huge and no one ever heard of a little rattlesnake. But let's be specific, even though we start a few mild fist fights.

Snakes don't charm victims. I can hear a dozen people say, "The hell they don't!" Birds do flutter about in front of snakes. I've seen it, and I've also seen a mother catbird whip the daylights out of a six-foot blacksnake. The fluttering merely draws the snake away from the nest of what we may think is a charmed bird.

Snakes can't spring into the air. They just aren't built that way. Next time you hear a fellow tell of a rattlesnake springing at him, risk a black eye by asking what brand he drinks.

Blacksnakes won't wrap and squeeze you nor will they "whip you," but in old wives tales they've been doing both longer than they have been milking cows. When I think back over some of the bossies that have kicked the daylights out of me, I can't quite see them standing quietly while a blacksnake takes on a free meal of milk.

Even newspapers now report that a rattlesnake had "eight rattles and a button." The button seems to be a sort of "may be and may not be" affair. That "button," gentle reader, is the next rattle which will emerge next time Mr. Rattlesnake sheds his skin, and all rattlers have them, from birth to death. Neither do eight rattlers indicate eight years of age. A new rattle comes with each shedding of the skin and this may occur two or three times in one summer. Also, seldom does a large snake have all his rattles. He loses them quite often.

While we're on the rattlesnake let's explode another myth. The timber rattler is of two unexplained color phases. One color is not male and the other female. Nature simply gave them two styles of coloring. She did the same for our little screech owl.

Snakes are not blind in dog days. I doubt that they even know about dog days. The scale above a snake's eye will loosen and hang over the eye when the skin is about to be shed. That may be at any time during the summer and may last only a short time. Don't go about during dog days kicking blind snakes around. You may meet one that has lost his calendar.

176

They used to tell me that if I killed a rattlesnake and left it at the place its mate would be beside the dead body before sundown. Such marital devotion is truly touching, but all the snakes I tried it on must have been old maids, bachelors or widows.

Some folks also told me a rattler could not strike except from a coiled position. Truth of the matter is that the part of a snake's body that is formed into a circle can't be used in striking at all. Only that portion of neck and body that is an S shape is used in the strike. Don't pay much mind to a rattler's position anyhow. He can change it darn quick.

Another little caution, don't try to make a poison snake "safe" by pulling the fangs. New ones are lined up behind the front ones and come into use within a very few days. I have seen rattlers that had two on each side. Apparently a new fang was in the act of pushing an old one out.

This couldn't be complete without the old one of the blacksnake, which fights with a rattler and after each bite received, eats a piece of a certain plant to prevent poisoning. He sort of reminds me of Popeye and his ever present can of spinach. The venom of a rattlesnake only works on warm blooded creatures. So the cold blooded blacksnake is safe and doesn't need any "greens" to prevent poison.

Mention of cold blood brings to mind that many people describe touching a snake as "his hand felt something cold and slimy." Brother that was not a snake. Snakes are not slimy. They are dry to the touch. As for the cold part, there should be no sensation of temperature since snakes are as warm or as cold as the air about them.

Taking them all in all, snakes are a much mistreated group of reptiles. In reality, few are harmful, many are beneficial and all are very interesting to the person who cares to study them.

Now I'd better stop this before I slip and say that snakes don't swallow their young. That would cause one of the dangdest fights since John L. Sullivan retired.

INTUITION

When I left home for my daily grind one day last week, I noticed that one of my cows was acting very much like an applicant for a place in a bovine maternity ward. In the evening she was not at the barn so I started out to find her. At the far side of the pasture I spotted Old Betsy and she was proudly caring for a new calf.

When I was still thirty feet or more from the cow and calf there was a scramble under a small bush just a matter of four feet from the cow's heels and out dashed a rabbit. (He's the last survivor of his genus in this section of the country.) Examination of the dead bush showed a well defined and very cozy form in the grass that had grown up through the protecting bush. Now in case that word "form" slows any reader up; a form is the place where a rabbit sits on his fanny all through the daylight hours. Frequently Brer Rabbit may return to the same form many times. The ground may even become bare and smooth from his occupancy of the same place.

However, I didn't start to talk about rabbit forms. There was plenty of evidence that the cow had given birth to her calf on that particular spot. I estimated that she had spent at least four or five hours there. The ground was tramped full of tracks, some of which were within eighteen inches of the rabbit's hiding place. The question arises, "Just how nosy can you get?"

It looked to me as though the fact that the bush was a cut thorn bush with good spines was all that saved the rabbit from being tramped on repeatedly. Yet, he broke from cover when I was thirty or more feet away. Why the utter lack of fear of a laboring cow and the complete fear of man? Or maybe a better question would be, "How does a lowly cottontail rabbit know the difference between man and other animals?"

True, the cow and rabbit have grazed together all summer in the pasture and the cow has never harmed the rabbit. On the other hand, neither have I harmed him. I won't kill any wild thing close to my home nor permit others to do so. I like them close for study.

One opossum and a skunk seem to have accepted me to a

limited degree. They stay under my woodshed and come out during the first hour of darkness for their nightly handout. They both seem fairly chummy with my wife's cats but though they come for their food in the glare of a floodlight they usually make a dignified withdrawal if I get too close. I can understand this tameness somewhat, for an opossum is stupid and a skunk knows no one is going to argue with him at close range.

Red squirrels, too, are quite familiar about the place. Yet, although they go freely into my buildings with theft in mind, they still won't fully trust me.

Even domestic animals and birds seem to understand that man is to be feared. I have noticed that cows fear a stranger around the barn. I, also, have noticed that a cow knows something is wrong if her owner tries to put her in the barn at the wrong time of day. Milking time is ok, but any other time spells trouble to old bossy's sensitive mind.

Chickens may tramp all over the owner's feet when he goes about the poultry house on routine trips. They may have to be pushed out of the way. Yet, if the same owner goes into the coop and starts looking the flock over to select a nice one to kill for Sunday dinner, the whole flock instantly become wary. They withdraw to the far side of the coop and run when approached. Can a chicken read the human mind?

Can an old hen know when her owner has evil intentions? Some women have this power in regards to their husbands, but with poultry I believe the males have intuition, too.

We may say and usually do say that instinct tells lower creatures what things to fear. Now just what is instinct? It must be something super because it can even read intentions.

In Africa great herds of grass eaters mingle freely together. A plain may be covered with thousands of animals. Yet, Walt Disney pictures show us lions moving about very near to the grass eaters without causing undue alarm. That happens when the big cats are not hungry.

Then Mr. and Mrs. Lion start out for food and the animals seem to know it's time to move. Can they detect the intentions of the big cat?

The whole problem is one I just can't figure out. Really there are two parts to the question. First, how can the lowly creatures spot the probable danger? Second, why can't man be as smart as a rabbit? With all of our so-called brains we still can't tell which things we should fear and which we should trust.

****

WILDLIFE'S WORST ENEMY

Many years ago it pleased my "young man's fancy" to operate a trap line through a mountainous section of country where man had not made roads or homesites. In one place, at least two miles airline from the nearest house, I made a fox set. I caught no foxes there but I did catch four of the biggest and meanest house cats I have ever seen. All four were marked in similar colors and had the appearance of being litter mates. I don't believe any of them had ever known the refining influence of man's habitation. In brief they were true wild house cats, born in the woods.

I have often wondered how many birds, rabbits, squirrels and the like went into the diet that brought all of the four to a weight of around ten pounds each. When we also consider the fact that the domestic cat kills for pleasure whether hungry or not we must assume that those four had done real damage in their time.

Now let each reader recall for a minute how many cats he has seen along roads in lonely stretches on recent night drives. The answer can only be "too many."

Next let's make a check with hunters who go into the woods when there is snow on the ground. How many cat tracks do they see? Chances are there are more cat signs than game signs. And it matters little how far back one may go. The cat is there. His damage to game and bird population has been going right along for he knows no closed seasons.

Coon hunters are seldom surprised when the coon their dog has treed turns out to be another cat. Fortunately, few coon hunters leave these game menaces among the living.

All up and down our state we hear a clamor to the effect that foxes are eating our game. True, a fox does eat game when and if he can catch it. But he gets a lot more blame than he does game. Reynard harvests the credit for plenty of destruction that should rest squarely upon our dear little pussy cat. The one fact alone that the diet of the fox is about five times as varied as that of a cat puts the fox in second place to the meat eating cat.

180

What can a cat do for game? Plenty! He can kill a full grown rabbit with ease. A quail roosting on the ground is a picnic and even the toughest gray squirrel would have no chance against him.

I once flushed a wild house cat out of a small clump of alders. Inside that clump I found a regular summertime lair. That cat really had a cozy corner nest there. What was more to be noted was that remains of our young muskrats from a nearby marsh were scattered about the place. Not one was as much as half eaten.

Where do all the wild house cats come from? That's an easy one. Within the month you'll likely hear a neighbor say, "Puss is getting to be such a nuisance about the house, I suppose I'll just have to take her along on our next trip and drop her somewhere." Should you suggest a quick death instead you would create real horror. To kill an unwanted cat is cruel! Nice civilized folks just can't do that. It's much nicer to haul the unwanted cat out to a wooded area and leave it. It can find another home or shift for itself in the woods.

Likely half of the cats thus abandoned die a slow, miserable death of starvation. The more capable ones go wild and become predators of the worst sort. They roam the woods and feed upon game and birds until some hunter's gun ends their careers.

Near a roadside dump I once found four half-grown cats. All were lean, sore eyed and miserable. On another occasion I found, on a roadside, a sack that moved. Tied up inside the sack were four kittens. All these were put out there to starve by nice kindhearted people. Such kindhearted folks they were that they just couldn't kill the poor things. That would be too cruel.

I don't expect to make any laws or sit in any great legislative bodies, but if I ever do, I'll try hard to place a law on the books providing a stiff penalty for anyone convicted of abandoning cats along our highways. Such tenderhearted people should get about thirty days of solitary confinement with a tom cat orchestra on a nearby fence to keep them awake each night. The confinement would have to be solitary. Those people just couldn't bear to watch others suffer.

181

BRINGING HOME THE COWS

When I was a kid my entire life in summer was divided into twelve-hour parts. Each twelve hours was the distance between time for going out to hunt the cows for their twice daily milking. We always kept cows. We'd have been lost without them. Furthermore, we always kept cows that had a trait in common. That trait was that they never came in of their own accord. Other people, I knew, had cows that came home at milking time. Ours never did. No bawling calf, no pangs of hunger, no pressure on the udder ever swayed one of these distance minded brutes. They came home with me behind them, or else they stayed out.

We had no fenced pasture in those days. Neither did anyone else who chose to keep a cow in a busy sawmill town. Their ladyships were footloose and fancy free. The horizon was their limit. Some called it grazing on the "town commons." It was more like grazing on half a county. Many were the times when I found those brutes as far as two miles from home, and on special occasions as much as three good country miles lay between them and the barn.

Sometimes yet, when I think of those trips, I wonder why we didn't eat beef instead of drinking milk. Again I wonder why in hades I still keep cows. Memory should cure me of the habit even though I do now keep them in a fenced pasture.

Those memories are well studded with stormy evenings when thunder rolled and lightning flashed in jagged pitchforks through the sky. There were days of steady drizzle when every bush and weed drooped. (On such evenings my bovine friends were always found in thickets.) However, there were many more mornings and evenings when nature was at her smiling best.

When I recall how much of nature I learned on those pleasant evenings and dew sprinkled mornings, I'm inclined to think I'd do it all over again if I had the chance. Most certainly I'd still learn, for there is no nook or cranny in her range into which a cow will not poke her inquisitive nose, nor is there a thicket she won't use as a hiding place sooner or later.

On a great many occasions I had company. Bill, Joe and Ed

could often be talked into going along. Then the trip was slower but more fun. Four boys could find more to do than one. Often a snake could be caught and tormented, or my dog, Spot, a constant member of the party, might tree a groundhog, corner a skunk or even find a rattlesnake for us to capture. On occasions when our search led us to the lumber town just below our own we could be confident of a gang fight with a certain family there. Those boys were not too good with fists but they were Dead-eye Dicks with a rock. It paid to fight them close range.

Cow hunting was not merely bringing in a drove of unwilling brutes. Each trip was a natural history foray itself. Only now, looking backward, do I realize how many things of interest were found and experienced on those twice daily jaunts. The first blue jay nest I ever found was a good example. The nest was at a point where my route passed almost every day, and that old girl got so used to my inspections that she grew quite tame. From the first building until the young birds took the air I think that nest was looked over at least once every other day.

My dog's reaction to a shot in the eyes from a deadshot skunk made another memorable day. A mother opossum caught carrying a pouch full of young delayed milking time fully an hour. On another evening a big turtle digging a nest in the sand held our attention for an hour, and the eggs in the nest called for many visits there at later dates.

If the river got low we looked along it for fish. Sometimes we spotted a few good ones and at other times, not being too scrupulous, we "fingered" them then and there.

One occasion I shall never forget. We came to the bank of a deep backwater that extended back from the creek. We were prospecting for muskrat signs but what we found was a place full of bluegills, a fish not common then. We had no fish poles and couldn't "finger" fish in such water. I did have a hook in my straw hat. Ed was along that evening and was, for a change, wearing shoes. My hook, Ed's shoe string, and a cut pole and pieces of "crawdad" tails for bait resulted in a fine catch of bluegills and a late milking hour.

On another afternoon I learned a valuable lesson. Sport treed a groundhog in a little white walnut. I climbed up and grabbed him. I learned that groundhogs have teeth and know how to use them. I let Spot finish the job.

If we could get a strange boy to go along some evening we took him to our Indian turnip patch, our name for jack-in-the-
183

pulpit. The newcomer was told how good the roots were and usually induced to try one. With luck on his side he could get rid of the burning in his mouth in about four hours. At least once an irate parent got the entire gang licked at home for "trying to poison her boy."

Nearly all of the summer months there was something edible to be found. Berries started with the first tiny wild strawberries early in June and ended with blackberries late in August. Green apples from seedling trees could be eaten from July on. Thinking back now I wonder how any boy had enough cast iron lining in his stomach to eat those wormy little bellyaches, but eat them we did.

Birch bark was always good. In late summer when the bark didn't slip well we chewed the entire new tips. Today I don't think kids eat either green apples or birch bark. Maybe the human race is changing. I now see parents coaxing children to eat. Mine had a tough time finding me enough to eat.

May apples we ate but I don't believe we liked them. We also ate sour grass. I still like it. Tea leaves when they were young and tender were delicious. The berries were better yet. In brief, I don't think we passed up anything that could be eaten. The strange summer diet finally wound up in October with chestnuts, blackhaws and wild grapes that were properly frosted.

Longfellow wrote:

"A boy's will is the wind's will,
"And the thoughts of youth are long long thoughts."

I think Longfellow must have hunted cows in his boyhood. Certainly cow hunting is as free as the wind and on lazy afternoons the thoughts of a boy are long, long thoughts. Great thoughts and beautiful castles took shape in my mind as I trailed those brutes. They broke like bubbles but were lovely while they lasted.

Greatest of all the results of cow hunting was the outdoor knowledge that was picked up. Bit by bit it fitted into my mind to help make sense of the great jigsaw puzzle of Mother Nature. The puzzle lacks a lot of being finished. It never will be finished, but no matter how much of it I may put together my cow hunting trips will have contributed many of the pieces.

184

****

FEAR THE WOODS

William Cullen Bryant in his poem "Inscription for the Entrance of a Wood" gives this invitation:
"Stranger, if thou hast learned a truth that needs no school of
long experience,
That the world is full of guilt and misery,
And has seen enough of all its sorrows, crimes and cares to tire
thee of it,
Enter this wood and view the haunts of nature."

The poem goes on to tell us that here we may find peace and contentment for our world-battered nerves. He expressed a great truth: a truth that is as real in our day as it was in the days of Bryant. A trip to the woods which lie all about most of us can do wonders at putting mortal man at peace with self and the world about him. Unfortunately many people never discover the great healing spring of forest trees.

The fact of the matter is that many of us are just plain scared of a forest. We enter into its cooling shade and not peace but fear grips us. It is a fear so very real and of such magnitude that many avoid wooded areas altogether and others, finding themselves alone in the woods, become obsessed with such unreasoning fear that they actually become frantic to the point of giving up all mental control.

One adult man of seeming good mental balance told me of running wildly through a four-mile stretch of woods for fear of being caught there by darkness. It took him two days to recover from the overexertion of that run. I was once asked by four men if rattlesnakes were ever found on a certain trout stream. When I answered that one was found occasionally all four left the stream.

In a crowd of people with whom we might make a woodland trip there will be those who are ill at ease and worried in spite of the presence of others. There will be sighs of relief when the welcome road and waiting car comes into sight. Many hunters who go afield regularly still fear to get too far from a highway. As a result "road watchers" are all too numerous while a mile or two back game sleeps in peace.

Now just what is it that man fears in the woods? Some have
185

definite answers. Snakes are one of the common fears. In spite of the very small possibility of encountering a poisonous reptile and the ease of providing ample protection against such danger Mr. Snake still keeps multitudes away from the woods. To make it more unreasonable very few of those who fear them have ever had any real experience with snakes. Those who have had encounters seldom fear the snakes. Those who are afraid frequently base their fears on tales they have heard from others.

Fear of wild animals keeps the next highest group away from the forest. In spite of all that naturalists write and say many people fully expect bears, wildcats and those extinct panthers to attack on sight and to gorge themselves on human flesh. Again the tall story of some local Ananias is the cause of the fear. Wild animals just don't eat the human race and man is the most feared of all creatures. Other creatures withdraw even at the slightest scent of his presence.

The danger of getting lost keeps many people outside the woods. It is a real danger but one that is highly over feared. By taking a few precautions and keeping a level head any woodsman should have no difficulty in our road laced woods of today. Full discussion of this subject is too long to be used here.

When the matter is summed up we find that most fears are of what we *think* may be there instead of what we know. It is the vaguely suspected or unknown that worries us. This unknown fear is proved pretty definitely by one fact. Thousands of people who enter the woods by daylight could not be forced into them at night. Like children who play about a room all day yet refuse to enter it at night, we fear the unknown things that may magically appear with the setting of the sun. Common sense tells us that the same things are present in daylight as are there at night.

We may safely suppose that many of us still hold some of the instinctive fears that have come down to us through all the ages from our primitive ancestors. For them there were real dangers lurking in the forest. However, the real dangers were slight compared to those that superstitious minds supplied. To primitive man the darkness of forests concealed a thousand dangers of ghost, beast, reptile and devil. Perhaps then as now the really great fears were of the unknown.

Then, too, as now, unknown things went about at night. Darkness covered the meanderings of ghost, goblin, witch, monster and beast. All such things we have discredited. Or have we?

Do we still carry a trace of the same fear of the unknown, the same awe of darkness, shadows or woods? I'm sure we do.

Do you doubt it? Try an experiment. Get twenty persons who stoutly deny any belief in ghosts or unknown things and see how many of them will go alone to the graveyard at night, to investigate a strange sound.

Man faces danger more bravely when he knows what it is. The worst possible actual danger becomes less when known than it was while still unknown. We just don't have quite the mental power to assess all possibilities and reduce them to their rightful proportions.

A more intangible fear that affects many is that of being in strange surroundings without the sustaining presence of other people. The escaped zoo leopard or tiger does not revel in his newfound freedom. The fears of the unknown woodland and the strange quiet sends him slinking back to the security of his cage. So it is with many people. Vaguely afraid of the unknown and quiet forest they tire soon and return to the noise and security of their city cages. There they find the life they know.

Why can't we face facts? Our forests are safe. There are no ravenous beasts, no vengeance seeking reptiles, no unknown goblins or demons. Instead there is peace, quiet and harmony of life. To man it all spells rest to the body and uplift for the soul. And just remember the words of William Wordsworth:

"Nature never did betray the heart that loved her."

****

GUTS OF SURVIVAL

Lately due to the invention of such lovely things as hydrogen bombs and guided missiles our world lives in a constant state of jitters. Every time the big noise from Moscow begins to bellow threats and pounds the desk with his shoes we renew talk of "survival." New plans are published for bomb shelters and Mr. Average Citizen begins to envy the groundhog and wonder if he'd like to entertain company.

For my own part I can't help but wonder, if I were to build a fine bomb shelter, would I be murdered for it by some kind gent who wanted it more than he desired my presence. That is,

187

of course, when the bombs began to drop. However, as to the survival angle there is a different story.

Newspapermen have recently carried accounts of survival tests in the woods. Some were on the level, some, likely, were hoaxes. Some were said to have proved the possibility of successful survival in wooded areas. Now it seems to me that we need no proof that the woods can provide the needs of man. Our ancestors proved that over and over. The only proof we need now is whether or not we are as resourceful as our ancestors were.

Great-great-grandpa may have moved into a new region with little more worldly goods than what he could carry on a packhorse. Most important of which was an axe and rifle. He expected the woods to keep him until he got settled or until an Indian arrow sent him to celestial lands.

Right off the bat the forest gave him a crude shelter in the form of a log house with clapboard roof. It gave him split log benches, tables and other needed furniture. The forest also fed him.

At this point some reader will grin wisely and remark, "But there was lots of game then." Old travel accounts don't back that belief too well. Many explorers lived more by fish than by game. The virgin forest with its towering trees and scant undergrowth didn't support as much game as we are often led to believe. Not until early settlers made openings in the woods and gave to game a needed browsing area did large populations of deer and other game come into the picture. Today's deer herds, for example, are estimated to be far larger than when Columbus first nosed into the new world.

The pioneer ate meat. It was his staple. It consisted of fish, deer, bear, raccoon, opossum, squirrel, grouse, rabbit, groundhog, turtle, and perhaps others. However, very likely, there was more than one Friday in each week. He couldn't always have what he desired. Somebody has said that the pioneer mother often handed her son a rifle and said, "Son, go out and shoot us some meat. If you miss, don't hurry back to dinner. There won't be any."

Meat was not the only food the forest gave. Our ancestors made great use of nuts of all varieties. Not only did they eat such as the hickory nut and walnut but the mast of the oak fattened their hogs after they "got settled." The native chestnut was almost a staple. No turkey was complete if not stuffed with chestnuts and the same nut was life to game.

Berries were important. Great quantities of blackberries, strawberries, raspberries, and blueberries were gathered. The blueberry or huckleberry was a favorite because it could be dried easily for winter use. Wild grapes, also, could be dried.

From early spring until late summer greens were gathered from both woods and open places. Poke, dandelion, rock lettuce, wild beet, lamb's quarter, mustard and a host of others went into that grand mixture. Some housewives insisted on the right amount of each to bring about the proper blend. Others liked each one alone with no mixture.

For sweetening the pioneer tapped the big sugar trees of the woodland or on rare occasions the finding of a bee tree added a real treat. No homestead was complete without its sugar orchard and hewn troughs for catching sugar water.

The skins of deer were used for clothing or leather, and tanned with hair on, made a cover. However, the prize winter cover was a bear skin. As for hats, in those days all self-respecting raccoons expected to wind up adorning some pioneer's head.

Naturally, the early settler got sick occasionally. Naturally, also, he knew he had to be his own doctor and the woods must furnish his medicine. Boiled cherry bark made cough syrup as, also, did scraped bark of the sycamore. Catnip tea was good for ailments as varied as the people who made it. When a youngster got a bad cold, one cup of boneset tea either cured him or made him such a liar that he never again admitted to having the sniffles.

Mandrake roots and golden seal had their places in the medicine cabinet, and the supposedly poisonous poke berries made a gargle for whooping cough victims. The root of the poke had its medicinal uses for the human race and buckets full of it were fed to sick cows. Other things used were bloodroot, pine resin, spruce gum, huckleberry roots, ginseng, teaberry and many more. Bleeding was checked by use of a puff ball, nasal colds were cured by smoking mullen and a pregnant woman just had to have a tonic of turkey berry tea.

Once the settler got a garden and corn patch going he lived the life of Riley. The woods about him furnished the rest of his daily needs. The woods are still here. They still grow pretty much the same things. Question: Could we of today survive for a few weeks left in the woods on our own resourcefulness?

To say the least we overlook some bets in good eating if we don't take advantage of the woods around us. There is still available to the hunter a pretty wide variety of meats. Some of these may never have been tried by a large part of our people. Just forget those scruples and try a good chunk of fried ground-hog along with a side dish of greens, a cup of sassafras tea, one good slab of cornbread and for dessert a dish of wild raspberries. As an old friend of mine used to say, "That's a meal to make a man slap his own grandma."

****

SPARE THAT DEN TREE

Once I travelled through a particular section of one of our fifty-five counties with an elderly character. He was an old gentleman who knew the country well. At one point he stopped and pointed to a small stump. "Now there's a stump that made history," he said.

Naturally, I inquired the reason. I got this interesting story. It seemed thereabout in days gone by there had lived a Rip Van Winkle sort of couple. The husband, like Irving's Rip, was badly henpecked. On occasions the "lady" of the house might pick up any sort of weapon and clobber the husband unmercifully.

On the occasion of the story she had flown into a violent rage and seized a double bitted axe. The husband fled as fast as legs would carry him with the angered wife in hot pursuit. As the chase led up a narrow hollow the man realized he was losing ground and like an animal in front of the hounds he treed. Perched in the top of the small tree he watched his wife at the foot. She could run and fight but couldn't climb.

Just when the husband began to feel secure in his perch his wife realized that an axe was for other purposes as well as for dividing a husband. With might and main she began to chop. Seeing the new development below, the cornered man pulled out his pocket knife and started trimming a convenient limb into a club. When the tree was ready to fall the club was also ready.

In a swirl of branches the tree fell to the earth. Into the fallen

190

top the wife charged with axe held high. But the worm had turned. The husband emerged unhurt and with his club succeeded in disarming his soul mate. Then he played a tattoo on the back portion of her anatomy the whole way back home. According to my informant she became a dutiful wife thereafter.

Some wag must have had this story in mind when he wrote this parody on a familiar poem.

> "Woodman spare that tree,
> Touch not a single bough.
> It's the only one my wife can't climb,
> And I'll protect it now."

All this is only to add a bit of emphasis to a simple request. I might make a parody too.

> "Woodman spare that den tree,
> Hunter stay away, too.
> A home in the wild for many a year,
> It's a thing of profit for you."

For many years now game management men and government foresters have recognized the value of den trees. It seems that squirrels, raccoons, owls, opossum and the like need homes in large dead trees with hollows in them. There they find security and raise their young.

Wild things are not always segregationists. In one old tree we may find a den of raccoons. In a smaller hollow higher up a mother gray squirrel may be rearing a brood, while in a hollow limb there may be a family of screech owls, woodpeckers or flying squirrels. Under the aged roots there may be a woodchuck den, now used by an interloping family of skunks.

Unfortunately animals when chased frequently head for the security of such trees. Then, unfortunately again, many hunters are not sportsmen. The old den tree may be cut down for the sake of a fifty cent coon or, worse yet, a careless person attempts to smoke out a victim and not only burns up the tree but a whole forest as well. The fact that it is unlawful to destroy a den tree makes little difference to many hunters. The results are a growing shortage of suitable homing trees for the wild. Shortage of homes means a decreasing supply of game. Every hunter who protects a den tree is protecting the future of his own sport.

191

The old dead tree does not constitute a growth problem in the woods. Its roots are dead, too. They take no nourishment from the soil. They cast but little shade. Young growth grows all around the old dead monarch.

Many coon hunters hate the hollow tree because the coon gets inside where he can't be spotted. Let's remember that some of a species must escape to carry on the race. Besides, what is any sport that has no hazards and gives the opposition no chance? Let's just spare that den tree.

****

THE HUNTER THAT ALWAYS WINS

I hesitate to write this article. I know that many readers are going to brand me the biggest liar since Ananias' time and somehow I don't like being called a fibber of such proportions. I think, though, that the truths of nature are so much stranger than the fiction that is written about her that most people who tell the plain truth are likely to be called liars.

Shakespeare wrote:

"Travellers ne'er did lie, Though fools at home condemn them."

Marco Polo could vouch for that one. When he wrote the account of his world travels and told of the animal wonders he had seen, his readers thought him to be a very entertaining liar. His account of that fat-tailed sheep of Asia caused belly laughs all over Europe.

Now I'm going to write about a very little fellow. He weighs only a few ounces. His slim body won't measure a foot in length. He can go through an ordinary knot hole. But brother, he's tough and he's mean. I'm talking about our common weasel. Ounce for pound he'll hold his own against all comers. And to prove my "ounce for pound" statement, a six-ounce weasel will kill a six-pound hen with impunity.

My earliest introduction to the weasel came when I was but five years old. My sister, who was about sixteen, and a girl friend of the same age took me for an afternoon walk along a narrow country road. At one point the road clung precariously to a high hillside with an almost sheer drop of two hundred feet on one side. At this point we noticed a large rabbit lying on a

192

flat stone at the very edge of the road. It was kicking a very feeble farewell to life. Not until we stood directly above it did we notice the tiny weasel with teeth clamped in the rabbit's throat. His beady little eyes stared unafraid at us out of the rabbit's fur. Neither our voices nor threatening motions caused him to give an inch. Even when a stick was thrown at him he stubbornly held onto his prey.

While I stared at the little monster bug-eyed, one of the girls, with her foot, slid the flat rock, with its outdoor drama still on it, over the edge of the road. My last sight of the incident was of the rabbit and weasel turning cartwheels down that steep slope with the throathold of the killer still intact. I feel sure he finished his meal somewhere at the bottom.

On another occasion I found a mute testimony to the tenacity of the weasel. I was walking along a railroad track near some scattered houses when I noticed the body of a young chicken lying beside one of the rails. The chicken had not been touched by train wheels. The head and the teeth of the weasel were clamped in the chicken's throat. On the other side of the rail lay the hind legs and tail. That tough guy had stood his ground against a freight train. Neither did his teeth let go when his body was cut in two parts.

Several years ago I planted a small patch of corn at some distance from the house. A day or two after the planting I discovered that a small regiment of chipmunks were digging up my seed. Along the edge of the patch I placed several mouse traps, each baited with a grain of corn, and each tied to the fence with a stout cord.

The day after the traps were set a nephew came along with his twenty-two rifle and informed me that he was on his way to rid my corn patch of chipmunks. In a short time he was back. In his hand he carried a live weasel which he was gripping around the neck. The weasel was holding, with a bulldog grip, a chipmunk and the chipmunk was in one of my traps. That weasel had been carried more than five hundred yards and still showed no inclination to let loose the meal he had been caught pilfering from my mouse trap. For experiment I held the trap and told my nephew to let loose of the weasel. It made no difference. That weasel clung to his chipmunk even when swung through the air like a pendulum.

Somewhere I read of a great horned owl being killed. A

weasel skull was found among the throat feathers. The teeth were clamped in the owl's skin. Somehow the owl had succeeded in killing his attacker, but the tenacious little beast held on even to death. How long the owl had been carrying that little skull for a locket was anybody's guess.

When a weasel takes the trail of an intended victim, that poor creature had just about as well give up. The ruthless killer can trail like a hound. He's cool and deliberate about his trailing and he has the patience to stay on the track for hours if necessary. Sooner or later his quarry will tire or go to a hole. If he tires, he's caught above ground. If he goes into a hole, he's cornered, for anywhere he can go the weasel can go better.

One morning I was in my barn milking when a big rat emerged from a hole in the floor. He climbed an upright two by four to the plate on which the cross beams rested and travelled around two sides of the barn. Then he came down to where a set of harness hung against the wall. For the rest of his descent he used the harness and finished by following down a swinging tug. On the floor again he disappeared down another hole.

Thirty seconds later a weasel emerged from the same hole through which the rat had come. With never a pause of indecisive motion he followed the exact path of the rat to the last detail and disappeared into the same hole where his victim had gone. I counted off one rat and perhaps many more. For several weeks after that I saw no rats around the barn.

The persistence of the weasel on a trail was well illustrated to me on an occasion when a group of berry pickers was waiting at the top of Cheat for a log train. Near the track a big pile of trash lumber had been dumped in a disordered pile. We were attracted by the sight of two or three young snowshoe rabbits darting out of the pile and back into it at different places. Going closer, we saw a weasel come out of the same place where a couple of the rabbits had come out. He followed to where they had returned to shelter and darted into the pile.

Several of us gathered rocks and watched for the reappearance of the young rabbits. Sure enough they continued to come out and go back. Each time the rabbits came out the weasel was not far behind. Each time he showed he was met with a hail of rocks. None hit him. However, the barrage did prevent his following the trails outside the lumber heap. Nevertheless, he still sought his prey among the timbers and showed himself quite

194

often. When Shay engine number eight whistled we had to leave. I'm sure that weasel had a rabbit for supper that night.

When we add to the trailing ability and the tenacity of the weasel, the fact that he's the most blood thirsty little demon in our woods, we have a real killer. For some reason he loves to kill. He's no conservationist and he saves nothing for tomorrow that he can kill today. He may kill an entire nest of young rabbits when he could scarcely eat one. In a coop of young chickens he's been known to kill half a hundred in one night. He may suck a little blood from a few of them but most are simply killed and left untouched.

In a fight each ounce of weasel is good for a pound of nearly any other type of predator. The owl that seizes one is frequently brought low by the intended victim. The average house cat that mistakenly grabs the little villain usually retires a sadder and wiser cat. I even saw a trapped weasel give a good account of himself against a small dog though he was hindered by the trap on one leg.

All in all, Mr. Weasel is just about as tough as they come. One coon hunter whose two hounds had caught a weasel remarked, "If that little devil had weighed five pounds he'd have whipped both dogs and me to boot."

****

SUPERSTITIONS

Every mountaineer worthy of his jug of moonshine has a number of signs, omens, superstitions and strange beliefs tucked away in his mind. These same phenomena, in many cases, govern a large part of his life. Just how many are well founded, how many are superstitions and how many are pure bunk handed down from the days of witchcraft?

The harmless old man in the moon comes in for a large share of our folk beliefs. Our word "lunatic" comes from the Latin "luna" meaning moon. Is the mentally unbalanced person really worse at the full of the moon?

Watch when you plant those potatoes! If they are planted in the light of the moon the crop will grow so near the surface they'll sunburn. On the other hand, plant in the dark phase and

195

the spuds will grow so deep you'll need a post hole digger to harvest them. You can't win on that one.

You can win on laying a rail fence. A fence built in the light of the moon will stay up well from the earth, but watch that dark period. Your fence then will sink into the ground and rot the bottom rail. Be careful too of putting shingles on a house. If the moon is light they will curl up like overcooked bacon slices.

How come a storm ever catches us napping? Look at the signs that foretell its coming. A hog builds a nest, rabbits head for the nearest holes and most wild things in general come out and eat a lot and then head for deep shelter. The owls get into the act, too. They hoot far into the morning. When they stop the cardinals take over and call "what cheer, what cheer" all day.

Livestock on the farm know all about the storms, too. Sheep and cattle eat all the hay you'll give them and stay close to the barn. Horses become skittish and hard to handle. They run and kick up their heels in great fashion and do a lot of unnecessary snorting and blowing.

The old moon comes out wearing a ring to denote the coming storm. Sometimes she even wears a misty veil. You just can't fool the moon or catch her unaware.

Let's not forget sounds. The rooster crows in the middle of the night before storms and he can be heard for great distances. At the same time a train whistle carries miles farther than usual. There's really no need to be caught by a storm.

Rain is important to man. How do we get it? Simple. Owls hoot in daytime, cardinals call, "rain crows" coo, and tree toads twitter. That's enough. Down she comes, in obedience to orders. But there's a catch or two. If it "starts before seven it quits before eleven" and if it rains on Monday, we must have four days of it that week. No wonder Friday is "fairest or foulest" of days. However this is nothing to good old dog days. Let dog days start wet and you'll need a raincoat for six weeks.

Now how about hard winters? Look at the warnings we get. Heavy coats of hair or fur on animals, thick corn shucks, early bird migrations, squirrels storing away many nuts, or lots of fat on groundhogs all tell that a hard winter is coming.

The gardner needs signs and omens. Without them he'd never get a crop. Therefore, he knows that a heavy service bloom means a good corn year coming up. He also knows that if he plants in the sign of the flower his plants will bloom their blooming heads off but set no fruit. On the other hand, if he plants in the sign of the twins he gets a double crop. But never plant in the sign of the virgin. It seems that virgins just aren't productive. If it's production you want get a pregnant woman to help with your garden. She'll make it a jackpot production. If you don't have one in your own family you just invite a pregnant neighbor over and escort her on a sight-seeing tour of your garden. Be sure to have her cover the garden well. The results will astound the believers and convince the nonbelievers.

At this point a word of caution should be inserted. Whatever you do, don't point at a little cucumber. Sure as you do the little fellow will sicken, turn a pasty yellow and die.

Some beliefs make me wonder a bit. For example I hear, "a deer when jumped always runs uphill." What happens when he gets to the top? Then too, there's this one, "a raccoon washes everything he eats." When he's feeding on acorns at the top of a high ridge he sure has a long way to go for dunking.

From the days of antiquity the hoot of an owl has been a death sign. Shakespeare calls him, "that fatal bellman which gives the sternest good night." Guess the belief is OK though. Somebody likely dies about as often as an owl hoots.

Master of all good sign givers is the groundhog. By simply casting a shadow he sets the weather for six weeks to come. He must be right. Never yet has my section of our state failed to have six weeks of bad weather after February second. If the sun fails on groundhog day, I think the little demon carries a shadow throwing lantern.

****

THE TRUE SPORTSMAN

Somewhere I once found some lines that went this way, "Now and again one runs across someone who is just a little bit different from the ordinary run of folks—clear eyed, interesting, clean minded, ambitious—always looking ahead to greater things—unselfish, kindly, quiet spoken, like someone who has always been used to living close to God. And you pack such a person away in your heart."

It has been my lot to meet some such men. Not too many of

197

them have crossed trails with me, but there have been enough of them to grow into a sort of composite chap in my mind. Now that the said chap has become fully developed, I find him to be an odd sort of guy in our modern world.

He's not odd in looks at all. In fact he may look like any sort of fellow. He may be fat or lean, young or old, little or big, rich or poor. It's that crazy set of traits he has that makes him such an odd individual.

To begin with he nearly always has a twinkle in his eye and a friendly smile. If you meet him on a stream or a forest trail he'll treat you as a friend even though he never saw you before in his life. If you are hungry, he'll split his last sandwich with you or divide his pack of cigarettes if you are out. All moderns know that's no way to act.

This goofy guy will hunt deer for the entire season without losing an hour, but when and if he gets one he'll quit right away. Then comes January and the same deer killer will spend half a day in any kind of weather rescuing a doe trapped in an icy stream or lake. Next summer he'll work hours caring for a road crippled fawn.

The same fellow will hunt for turkeys all during the open season and maybe never get a shot. Yet when comes February snows he'll put on snowshoes and hike five miles with a half bushel of grain to feed the same birds he tried so hard to kill.

With the same type of irrational conduct my man will hunt grouse with all the zeal of a maniac but will risk his neck by swerving a car to avoid hitting one.

This chap is a fisherman, too. He goes at fishing as though his living depends upon it. Yet when the day is done, he's turned loose more than he's kept. He's probably spent hours fishing for a big boy without results, but during that time has caught many little ones. The funny part is that he's treated each little trout as though it were a treasure of some sort. He's wet his hands before handling each one and removed the hook very carefully. Then the little fellow has been placed back into the stream.

Maybe on some lucky day my friend will catch that big one. Likely it's an old grandpa he's been after in that same pool for years. Of course he's elated. In fact, he's probably ready to quit now and go home. But as he leaves with the big boy in his creel he may look at that pool a trifle sadly. If you were near you

198

might hear him mutter, "The place will never be the same. Almost wish I hadn't got him."

My man may work hard to beat you in the field or on the stream, but he'll never take an unfair advantage to do it. What is more, if he fails and you come out on top, he'll shake your hand and really mean it.

This fellow doesn't want his fish easy to get or his birds tame, he likes them to be wary and wild. He even enjoys having a wily old buck outsmart him. It adds zest to the chase.

Along the same line he's had a great day in the woods if he's seen lots of game even though he's failed to kill anything. He's thrilled just to know it's there. And on a trout stream you'll see a smile crease his face every time he sees a school of two-inch trout fingerlings. He knows when they are present there's still sport for the future.

It's a fact that this strange guy can enjoy a completely fruit-less day afield or on a stream. There's simply so many other things to enjoy besides killing and catching. On such days he can watch a sunrise or sunset. He can enjoy autumn's beauty of color or springtime flowers. Maybe when fishing he can spot a mother grouse and her brood or see a doe and fawn come to the water to drink. There's always so much for him to be interested in.

My friend seems to love the very game he kills. For that reason he likes a quick, clean kill. He abhors crippling game, so he won't take long chances. He'd rather have an unhurt squirrel running about the woods than for the same squirrel to be dying of wounds in some hollow tree.

It is strange indeed to see this fellow leave the woods or stream. Before he leaves he invariably stops and removes his battered old hat. Then with his eyes on the lofty peaks above him he quietly whispers his thanks to the Maker of All Good Things.

This friend of mine does many other foolish things. So many that most folks think he's a little balmy. He really isn't though. He's merely a living proof that a thing called "Sportsman" can still be found somewhere besides in the dictionary.

(Now all the above was written at the request of a friend. He, for some reason, read my account of a game hog and claimed that I should, in all fairness, describe a real sportsman.)

****

THE HEADDRESS OF A BUCK

With deer season just around a, probably cold, corner, many deer hunters have their sleep disturbed by an endless procession of antler wearing bucks. Naturally each hunter dreams of dragging in one that carries a rack too big to go through the front door.

Then when the first day arrives each one goes out with all daydreams in order for that colossal rack. Maybe most of them are like me. I dream of a big rack for the first few hours. Then I begin to whittle off a point or two with each passing hour. Along toward five o'clock I'd be satisfied with any size "just so it's legal."

Here and now I'll thrust my turtle neck out and talk a bit about those much desired headdresses that bucks wear. Maybe I'll have a fallacy or two but isn't that what readers love to find?

To begin with I've always been surprised during my many years as a taxidermist to find literally hundreds of hunters who still stoutly disbelieve the idea that deer shed their antlers each year. Some seem to regard the fact as an old wives tale, something like toads causing warts.

Well, superfluous statement or not, they do shed the antlers each year. Old Mother Nature spends about six months growing, sharpening and polishing a set of fighting tools just so Mr. Buck can have them for about two weeks of action during the breeding season. Then, the season ended, she knocks off what is left of that fine set and gives the old boy's head a rest. Sometimes there's not too much left. Frequently points are broken in fights and sometimes one whole antler may be knocked off in a fight.

One time while I was skinning out the nose of a buck my knife hit something hard. With a pair of pliers I pulled from the upper part of the nose an antler point one and one-half inches long. There was no scar on the skin so I'm convinced that the point had been embedded in the deer's face for more than a year. I heard of another case wherein a point was found in a

200

buck's shoulder blade. Those fights must get vicious occasionally.

There is a common fallacy to the effect that a deer gets a new point for each year of age. The truth is that a buck of two years may have a full set of eight or ten points.

Studies made on park deer indicate that a buck of three years may have reached about as far as he will go antlerwise. From three to about nine years of age there will be little variation in antler size. After nine or ten years the size may even decline to a smaller size and number of points.

We must keep in mind that we are talking about park deer here. They have constant food and proper protection. Out in the wild such things as food shortage or extremes of weather may greatly influence antler size. After a very open winter we may expect generally good antlers the following fall. By the same token we may expect the average to be smaller after an extremely hard winter. A deer that is half starved in the spring isn't capable of growing the best headdress.

With the above generalities we, also, must remember that old bucks often grow large, crooked, malformed or unusual antlers.

One thing may come as a surprise to many people is the fact that a buck usually grows the same general type and formation of antler year after year. When "Dusty" Rhodes was caretaker of the Beaver Dam Refuge he had several deer that hung pretty closely about his headquarters. Among dozens of shed antlers that he had collected he had as many as three and four sets from the same deer. They were almost identical, year after year. I saw, also, a collection of antlers from one park deer covering a period of twelve years. From the third to the tenth year there was practically no variation in size or formation.

Ancestry may have a lot to do with form and type of antler. Many years ago when our deer herd was just beginning to build up I could tell a hunter what section of the county his deer was killed in by looking at the antlers. I think that one buck, surviving the near extinction period of the first part of the century, became the paternal ancestor of a whole region and marked the offsprings with antlers similar to his own. Now that the whole county has at least some deer the similarity is not so pronounced.

Hunters often puzzle over a malformed deer head. Usually a deformity is passed off as due to an injury while the antlers are growing. In some cases this is true. However, your taxidermist who skins out the skull can usually show you a deformed or defective skull to account for bad cases of malformed antlers. It seems that a straight symmetrical skull grows well-balanced antlers while a crooked misshapen skull may grow very poor ones. I have in my records many cases of badly formed antlers and in each case there was a corresponding deformity of the skull.

Game studies indicate that soil conditions may have much to do with antler size. Limestone sections are thought to produce better racks than regions which are deficient in lime. A good balance of all soil nutrients seems to be desirable for producing either big bodies or antlers.

****

SKUNKS AREN'T THE ONLY STINKERS

Not too many years ago enough stink was raised to make an army of skunks hide their heads in shame. The big smell-raising question was whether or not man descended from the monkey. I understand the matter was allowed to drop when the monkeys threatened a lawsuit on the grounds of defamation of character.

It is true that man has descended. He's descended so far that he may never get back up. Even the monkey admits that. But I, taking sides with the monk, agree that the descent was not from the long tailed breed. Man shows too many of the common qualities of the barnyard hog.

If you don't believe it just watch a few of your friends when they get into a spot where they can catch four or five times the daily limit of newly stocked trout. Watch those bristles rise and hear the satisfied grunts as each load is packed into a waiting car.

On another occasion you may find the same chaps in a hickory grove where a heavy concentration of squirrels has gathered. Just listen to the shotguns boom and take a peek at the bulging game pockets as Mr. Genus Homo proves his porcine ancestry beyond all doubt.

Man seems to have been created with a bad case of the wants. Starting with a certain apple tree in a certain garden we have continued to the present day trying to grab off a lot of things we never were supposed to have. No matter how much we have already we still want whatever the other fellow has.

In the world of natural resources we have carried a "grab what the other fellow has" idea to sorrowful extremes. Regardless of how many blessings we may have had in our own abundant land we just can't help trying to import plants, birds, animals and fish from other countries. We have had our lesson repeatedly but burnt children in these cases don't seem to dread the fire.

In spite of the fact that one typical midwest county of our nation had more than four times as many varieties of trees as all Europe, exclusive of Russia, we still had to import more. So with a batch of imports we brought the chestnut blight which cost us one of the most widespread and valuable species of native trees. The total value of the blunder can never be put into dollars and cents.

One might think that the lesson of the English sparrow would stop the importation of birds. Not so. True to our "want it all" nature we brought the starling. Year by year he now extends his range and the cost of his presence soars ever higher. We did get even with England. We sent them the gray squirrel which promptly became a pest over there.

Each year the carp take over more of our waterways and becomes a greater nuisance. Remember we brought him here. At home he ate water vegetation. Here he eats eggs of other fish.

The water hyacinth was pretty in its native land. For that matter it's pretty here. But we spend millions in our southern states trying to keep it under control.

What farmer does not pay an annual rat bill of large proportions? Rat damage is a multi-million dollar item in the U.S. Rat poison companies are big business. Let's not forget that our common and most destructive rat, known as the Norway rat, came here as a stowaway on ocean vessels.

The tragedy is that still we don't learn. In very recent years southern states imported the nutria, a giant size water rat. According to his proponents he was to do a great job of cleaning out lakes by removing vegetation. Already regrets are pouring in. The nutria does too much of a good job. Among many faults it now seems he likes farm crops very well. Also he breeds very fast and is hard to control. His cousin, the muskrat, a valuable furbearer, is being pushed out by the newcomer.

What's the moral of it all? Just this—every so often some individual or group raises a clamor for a new import. For example, since World War II there have been many demands that we import the small German deer which poaching GI's killed there. In each instance the qualities of the proposed import in its native land are extolled. Forgotten is the fact that a creature removed from its native habitat may change its ways of living and become the Dr. Jekyll and Mr. Hyde of nature's world.

It is true that some imported species have been successful. The ring-neck pheasant for example. The brown trout also has friends but some claim he destroys the native trout. All in all the total of our successful imports could not give benefit enough to pay interest on the loss of the American chestnut.

We could recall here the story of the dog which saw his own shadow in the water carrying a piece of meat. In his efforts to seize the meat from the shadow he lost that which he had in his mouth.

No country of the world was originally more blessed with natural gifts than the United States. Why can't we be satisfied and happy with what we have?

****

DO BIRDS AND ANIMALS TALK

The question is constantly being asked, "Do birds and animals talk?" I think they do. They show definitely that by certain sounds they convey certain meanings and those are quickly and easily understood by their own kind. In addition there are certain silent communications between them which are more difficult for us to grasp or believe but cause no trouble to them.

In many cases wild things and domesticated animals convey messages of varied meaning with the same sound or call as far as our ears can distinguish. To a fellow member of flock or herd a change of tone is clearly noted and understood.

To prove such contentions, I can cite only examples. Readers may not believe them but they have convinced me. One of the most spectacular incidents had to do with voice tone.

Many years ago I spent several months with an uncle in Florida. Around the small village where he lived scores of cattle ran free on unfenced lands. Early one morning a neighbor butchered a calf and immediately took the meat to a cooling place. A couple of hours later a lone cow found the fresh, bloody mess where the calf had been killed. She began to bawl. I think there was a difference in that bawling. At any rate it touched off the wildest melee I ever saw among cattle.

Scarcely had the one cow got in good tune until she was answered from almost every point of the compass. In a matter of minutes cattle were coming from everywhere. They came at a gallop and at every jump they answered the bellow of the first cow. They splashed through swamps and plowed through thickets. The straight course seemed the only acceptable course. Every cow brute around seemed to have gone berserk. Some were still coming in that wild run as much as a quarter of an hour after the first call had sounded. By that time more than a hundred had gathered at the slaughter scene. All were still bellowing, wild-eyed, and pawing the bloody ground. For more than an hour they milled about the spot. Then the din began to subside and gradually the herd scattered.

Now what kind of note in the bawl of the first cow brought such results? One thing certain, it was different. And very certain it was that every cow, steer and bull within hearing understood it.

Three summers ago I was fishing a section of the Greenbrier when I chanced to flush an owl from some willows on the river bank. As he flew up a lone crow spotted him and began to "caw" as he darted in pursuit. To my ear there was no difference between that cawing and that which I might hear each ten minutes from the surrounding woods. But, oh, brother, the results!

Instantly that crow was answered from all sides. I knew I was about to witness the start of one of those crow mob scenes I had seen many times before so I sat down to watch.

From every direction there came answers and crows. The call must have been relayed for miles and all the minutemen must have been ready. Within minutes there were dozens of crows cawing about a big hemlock into which the owl had flown. Inside of ten minutes there were hundreds, and stragglers were still joining the army. When the poor owl broke from the hemlock and fled, I believe that as many as five hundred black scoundrels were in the wild mob that pursued him.

On another occasion a friend and I were camped on Cheat River, when a young crow began to caw from a hundred yards above our camp. I raised my melodious voice in what my friend claims was the absolute world's worst imitation of a crow call. The young fellow answered me and left his place to come immediately to a tree directly over our heads. Simultaneously with his answer and start toward us two other crows, apparently his parents, began a wild clamor from farther away. They arrived above us almost with the youngster and literally snatching him out of the tree, they took him swiftly to a safe place on the other side of the river. There, if ever a young crow got told off, that one did. For full five minutes those oldsters talked to their offspring. I believe he was called every low-down name in crow language. I doubt that he would ever answer me again.

Once when driving on a hard road I stopped, very courteously, to allow a mother skunk and five youngsters to cross the road in front of me. The six were marching in a sedate single file order as precise as soldiers on parade. When directly in front of me the little buck private on the rear stopped and began to chase his own tail. The mother stopped and so did the other four young. Mamma turned and, going back, made a close circle around the playful youngster. Instantly he resumed his place at the end of the line. The old one took her place at the head and off marched the family. I don't know what the old girl said, but whatever it was she got results.

How does a cow or doe deer tell her young to lie down and remain in one spot until she returns? There's another effective order. Just find a calf where the old cow left it and try to make it get up. You get no results. Pick the calf up and you find its legs are rubber. They just won't stand under him. He was told to lie there and that's what he's going to do. But wait until the mother shows up. One low sound from her and the little fellow is up.

Do birds or animals of another kind understand their varied neighbors? Apparently, yes. Let a blue jay spot you in the woods where you are quietly waiting for game. Listen as he wildly announces your presence to all the world. Then see how much game shows up. I've had squirrels, on two occasions, coming toward me, and have seen them turn and run the other way when a blue jay began to call me all the names in the book. Those squirrels must have recognized the jay as an efficient watchman.

206

Old-timers have told me that a deer would turn away from a stand where a hunter was waiting when red squirrels were quarreling at the hopeful nimrod. I can't vouch for that one, and considering the deer and his hearing and scenting ability, I feel it would be hard to prove that the squirrel warned him. But one thing is certain, there's no greater talker in our woods than the fiery little red squirrel.

How do animals convey thought without sound? Hundreds of times I've seen one cow approach another. No sound is made, but the one cow being approached knows that the other wants to be licked. She has an itch where she herself can't scratch it. Not only does the second cow know the first wants to be licked, but she knows what spot is itching. I've seen this occur in cases where the one cow was an insufferable bully and the other deathly afraid of her. Yet somehow as the old bully approaches the cow she normally chases, she manages to say that this time she wants friendly service and not fight. The second understands and holds her ground where normally she would run.

All in all, our wild friends must have a pretty fair vocabulary. The fact that we don't understand them is our fault, not theirs. They get along with each other and they don't care about us.

****

ANIMAL FISHERMEN

Some time ago I did a column on bird fishermen. Several of my friends read it (why I don't know) and pronounced me a bigger liar than they ever thought I was. Others more kindly explained that I was getting old and not quite responsible for my statements. So with such encouragement I'll write about animal fishermen.

Really, there are quite a few furred denizens of our woods that look to the waters for a part of their living. Take the raccoon for example. He does have one of the widest diets of any native animal. No doubt, he could make out on mast, berries, meat and vegetation, but he prefers to have a few Fridays in his week so he is found along the streams very often.

When streams go nearly dry and fish are reduced to cramped living quarters the raccoon has a field day. With those two

207

hands of his he can scoop out fish both large and small with the greatest of ease.

When waters are high it is just too bad for the school of fish that may get stranded in backwaters. The raccoon knows all such places on his route and visits them faithfully.

When it comes to catching crayfish the 'coon is a master. He knows all about those flat rocks in shallow water and he knows all about the crayfish that stay under them. He will wade into several inches of water and select a likely looking rock. Then while his eyes, with apparent unconcern, look at all nature around him his forepaws probe beneath the rock. If the crayfish is under there he is a goner. He comes out clutched in a tight paw and is promptly washed and devoured.

The otter is, perhaps, master of good animal fishermen. With a speed beyond that of the water snake he glides after his prey. There is no sneaking up on a victim for him. He's a sportsman and gives his victim a chance. If the fish can out swim him OK, if not he's meat on the table. Usually he's meat, for the speedy otter is a weasel tribe member, and that tribe never gives up.

It is fascinating to watch an otter in a pool. He's streamlined grace from nose to tail. Speed is his middle name and he knew all about maneuverability before car makers ever heard of the word.

Our native mink is no slouch when it comes to the art of angling. A mink can glide into a pool and come out with a trout in less time than a dry fly fisherman can get his cast going. No use for fish to hide either. Nearly any place the fish can go the mink can follow.

I once watched a big mink on a small trout stream. I suppose he merely wanted to make me look silly. At any rate, he came directly to a pool where I had fished without result for several minutes. He glided into the water and was out of sight for no more than a minute. When he came out he had a small trout in his mouth.

Another time, I watched a mink exploring a backwater slough. The roots of a big birch had grown out well over the water at one place and I knew that several fish sheltered under there. The mink must have known it, too. He went straight to the place and went under the roots. There was a bit of gurgling and flopping heard and out came the mink with a rock bass.

The fish was taken directly up the bank to a caved in muskrat burrow. It took only a minute for the fish to be stored somewhere in that burrow and the mink was ready for more. In less than a quarter of an hour five fish were taken from under the birch roots and stored in the burrow. Then the mink went his way. He didn't stop to eat even one of his catch.

Who would ever suspect our lumbering bear of being a fisherman? He certainly doesn't appear built for it. Yet, he can wade into a pool and, with those big forepaws, flip fish onto dry land. His tactics are a bit rough and on the crude side, but he gets his fish. He cares nothing for lures or nylon lines. Fish on the table is all he cares about.

Here we run into an odd situation of nature. In our Pacific northwest, where the runs on salmon occur, the bears are eager fishermen. As the fish fight the currents up to spawning beds the bears take heavy toll of them. Then, when the spawning is over and the big fish die old bruin continues to eat the dead fish. He thrives on them. But the same dead fish are rank poison to a dog. Explain that to me.

****

THE FAIRY DIDDLE

Some years back a friend and I were deer hunting on top of Cheat Mountain. We had been on stands some distance apart and now it was time for me to go to my fellow hunter. As I approached him, I noticed that he was circling a huge dead tree with his eyes glued to the top and with his rifle raised at a ready position. Also he was swearing rather vociferously. The profanity seemed to be aimed at damning eternally all red squirrels. When I inquired the cause of his distress he pointed to a huge slab of dead bark lying at the foot of the tree and informed me that a blank, blank and double blank red squirrel had dislodged the piece of bark with such perfect aim that it had caught my buddy squarely across the back of the head. All he was asking now was to get that so and so in his rifle sights.

I suppose my friend was not the first deer hunter to waste a few naughty words on red squirrels. These pestiferous little demons love to be the tattletales of the woodland. Just go into the deer woods of our high counties and take a stand. In a matter of minutes a red squirrel or "fairy diddle" will spot you. Immediately he sees his duty and does it. He'll approach to within a few feet and proceed to "cuss" you with all the language at his command. He'll become so righteously indignant that he'll stamp all four feet for emphasis and the bad names will simply boil out of him. When he's through there won't be an insulting word left in his system. Neither will there be a bird or animal near that hasn't heard his tirade and, probably, taken warning of your presence.

In spite of it all the red squirrel is an interesting pest and we can learn a lot observing him. He's a true squirrel in spite of his diminutive size and squirrels have much in common regardless of color or name. His feeding needs and his habits are considerably like those of his larger cousins, the gray and fox squirrels. I believe he may eat a wider variety of food than the others and thrive where they fail. He's also much more pugnacious, more daring and ten times more impudent than the gray or fox variety. Otherwise, he's another squirrel, and now that our game division has put a regular season on him we'll have to grant him a certain status.

For the past several years I've had a number of red squirrels staying around my yard. My favorite comparison concerning them is that they are just like chiselers on relief rolls. I feed them all winter. They steal from me all summer and cuss me every time they see me. However, they do teach me a lot and furnish hours of entertainment.

Each summer about four or five litters of young are brought out from various holes in the trees about the house. Each female appears to have two litters a summer. Most of the young are driven away as soon as they reach a reasonable degree of self reliance but enough manage to stick around to keep the number on the increase.

A few times I've watched a mother move her young from one den tree to another. I can't figure why the move, but it is interesting to see. Mama catches her baby by the skin of his belly and the baby promptly curls himself around her head. With the baby, sometimes two-thirds as large as the mother, wrapped thus around her head or neck the mother appears to be wearing a huge fur neckpiece. She carries the youngsters with speed and apparent ease.

On one occasion, I was watching a young one that had ventured from the den tree to another one a few feet away. He seemed to be trying to get back to the home tree but couldn't

210

find the right limbs to follow. A quick summer shower was coming over the near hills. Whether the young one knew about the rain I don't know, but I think the old lady did. She suddenly appeared on the scene and went to the rescue of her stupid offspring. She was out of patience too. She ran into him rather hard and bowled him over on one side. Then she seized him by the belly skin and with him curled around her neck quickly carried him to the den. There she thrust the baby roughly into the den hole, backwards, and accompanied her task with what appeared to be cuffs with her front paws. It was definitely rough treatment for Junior and for an hour afterward he didn't so much as poke his nose out.

I find an odd situation concerning the "who can lick who" among red squirrels. It seems that they love to battle but I can see little evidence of any established system of bullying or supremacy. If a newcomer enters territory already occupied it seems that the first one there is boss. Usually he'll drive out the newcomer.

I put feed out for the squirrels in a flower pot suspended in a tree. If one is at the feeder he seems able to repulse any invader. However, if the one in possession leaves to bury a nut somewhere the other may take over. Then he seems to be Mr. Big and is able to keep the former occupant out.

How do squirrels know a nut is no good? I wonder if it is done by testing the texture of the outer shell. Hundreds of times I've watched those reds take nuts from the feeder. Never yet have I seen one leave with a nut until after he holds it in his paws and tests it with his teeth. It only takes a second or two, but if he goes away with it you may depend it's a good one. If he drops it you need not put it back; it's no good. Each of the discarded nuts will have the mark of teeth on it, just a light mark or two but it must be enough for him to know all he wants to know.

I sometimes wonder how many nuts a red squirrel would carry off and hide in a day. On one occasion, I placed about five quarts of hickory nuts in a basket on the front porch. There I assumed they'd be safe. That evening my wife and I came through the yard and saw a red making off from the basket with a hickory nut. I hadn't intended those nuts for squirrel food, so I started to get the basket to move it to a safe place. My wife called after me to give him some of the nuts. She thought he deserved a few for his daring. About that time I looked into the

211

basket. Give him some! I should have asked him for some. I had a scant handful left.

How wide is the variety of a red squirrel's menu I haven't yet discovered. He eats all varieties of nuts and seeds. He cuts apples to pieces to get at the seeds. He cuts big white pine cones down to a slim core. He eats thornberries and sassafras seeds as well as the berry of the gum tree. In spring he eats masses of oak bloom, spruce tips, buds of all descriptions and green service-berries. At times he eats birch bark.

I once threw out rinds from cured pork. Red squirrels carried them all away. One that I watched carried a piece so big it overbalanced him and he continued his journey along a limb hanging to it from underneath. Yet he didn't drop that fine big meat skin.

I once placed some pumpkins out with a one inch hole cut in them. The squirrels enlarged the holes and cleaned out all the seeds plus a lot of the pulp.

I couldn't close this without reference to one tragedy. A family of four little reds made their appearance outside a den hole near our kitchen window. For two or three days they were there, then we saw them no more. I wondered if they had moved and watched the tree rather closely. Then within a few days I saw the head and about a foot of the body of a black snake thrust out of the den hole. That answered all questions. A load of shot finished the snake and with a long pole, I pulled all six feet of him out of the hole. It was several weeks before a squirrel would enter that hole again. I would see them come to the edge of it and then leave there fast. I believe they could smell that snake.

****

BIRDS

Did you ever notice how many birds are like people? Let anywhere from a dozen to two thousand birds of a feather get together and just listen. Everyone talking at the same time and not one listening. Now compare that with an invited speaker struggling for attention at a big family reunion. Who's listening?

No one. Who's talking? Everyone. But I want to show that specific birds are like certain people.

Take our noisy blue jay for example. Each winter he swoops onto my bird feeding station with one intent: to get the "mostest, quickest." With unerring ability this hog of the feathered world seizes the biggest piece of food and takes off. Next trip, next biggest piece and so down to the smallest crumb. And does he eat as he goes? Only enough to keep life and vitality. He much prefers to hide and hoard food. His policy is to get it all before the next fellow gets a chance. He reminds me exactly of some game hogs I know.

Next watch that jay steal. He'd rather steal than get food honestly. The tiniest morsel packed in a crack by a chickadee is delicious if stolen. I've seen him steal hickory nuts hidden by squirrels but even his strong beak can't begin to penetrate the shell. That's stealing for the sake of stealing. Kleptomaniacs and out of season hunters take note.

That same old jay has yet another human trait. When spring rolls around all other feeders leave and go it on their own. But not the jay. He's like a chiseler in a commodity line. He'll come as long as you put it out and even after you quit he'll come for days just to make sure you haven't had a change of heart.

Another bird that gives me a chuckle is the diminutive wren. Just let me get too close to her nest and hear the names I'm called. Between savage darts at my head, she calls me every name in bird lore and dares me to fight in terms anyone can understand. She's half as big as my thumb but she states she can and will, if necessary, whip me and my family plus the tomcat. Did you ever notice how many fights are started by little guys? Maybe it's because they have little to lose. Chances are the big fellow won't hit the little one at all and if he does—well after all it's no disgrace to be beat up by a big bruiser like that. In the schoolroom I find that the big two-hundred-pound football fullback is a quiet gentleman. Most trouble comes from some little wart that can't get noticed any other way.

Like the human bully, our American eagle likes to pick on the osprey. Just let an osprey dive into the chilly water and come up with a fine fish dinner in the sight of the eagle. Watch old Baldy take after the poor guy and make him drop his fish and watch our noble bully catch it in midair while the osprey seeks again for a meal he may get to eat if the eagle has enough.

213

Somebody who knew more about poetry than he did about birds once wrote "Little birds in their nest agree." Phooey! A flock of birds do as much fighting among themselves as goes on at a political convention. If the world were covered with bird seed some birds would go insane trying to keep others out of it. Not only do those of one kind battle other varieties, but they can't even agree in the family. Each kind has its own established peck system and everyone knows his place in order. Everyone knows which brother he can lick and which one he has to run from. At my feeding station one winter I had an old cock of the roost cardinal that would sit around even after he was full just to show his rank by chasing others away.

When driving through some of the shack and shanty sections of our state I can't help thinking of the whippoorwill. There's a bird too lazy to build a nest so mama simply deposits her egg in any convenient spot on the ground and then sets up housekeeping.

At this point a lot of human mothers had better quit reading. I mean those that give birth to a child and promptly turn it loose on a defenseless society, allowing said kid to run the streets at all hours, to annoy all people and to receive what training it gets at the hands of teachers, social workers and instructors in the school of delinquency. These mothers are the cowbirds of the world.

The cowbird, too lazy to hunt for food, hangs around the head of a grazing cow and picks up the insects that are flushed by the cow's busy nose. When the hostess lies down to chew her cud the cowbird rests. Hence the name.

When it comes time for rearing young the cowbird does it the easy way again. The female simply deposits an egg in the nest of some smaller bird like the goldfinch or song sparrow. Then off she goes leaving the hatching and rearing task to the unsuspecting smaller bird.

Shortly after the young monster hatches he succeeds in snatching all the food brought in and starves out the rightful family. From then on to a rather delayed maturity he yells from morn to night for more food and nearly works the foster parent to death supplying him.

All in all birds are really quite human things. I'm glad they can't read. They might not like these comparisons.

214

WINTER CHISELERS

In this stepped up space age of ours things move around faster than a red squirrel on a grapevine. Some customs and pastimes seem to change or die completely. Then to our surprise they hop up again with a new shirt on and become popular fads. I thought the art of making apple butter was dead. Then suddenly a few years back my backyard blossomed out with the full force of my wife's church group and such apple butter making you never saw. It's an annual affair now and that apple butter goes far and wide while the returns fatten the church treasury. I'll do a column on that occasion before next fall.

What I want to get around to is how things change as years roll by and come up in a different light. The pioneers hunted wild game for food. That made hunting plain work. Now it's sport. Same goes for fishing. Once it was work, with food the chief aim. Now we spend the price of a good ham to catch a six-ounce trout.

You'd never guess it but what I started out to work into was the change in feeding winter birds. You don't have to be so very old to remember when newspapers carried those heart rendering appeals that urged you to feed our little feathered friends during the cold days of winter. The article would tell us about the value of a few bread crumbs to a starving bird and suggest a few little bits of suet for an additional staple. The housewife who fixed a window sill upon which to place a few such handouts felt very noble indeed.

Today bird feeding is not charity. It's, to say the least, a fad. We might even call it another outdoor sport. Certainly it has taken on many of the qualities of a legitimate sport. For example, it is commercialized now. No longer are a few crumbs placed on the window sill or scattered in the backyard. The window sill has been replaced by fancy feeders of all sorts. Following approved agricultural methods some are equipped with self-filling troughs. All are brightly painted and very attractive. They may even match the outdoor coloration scheme of house and grounds. Everyone knows that no self-respecting

215

woodpecker would eat at a joint where the color scheme clashed with his red head.

For the very lazy bird fancier there are those feeders which swing on a long extended arm on a pivot or operate on a miniature cable car arrangement. These may be refilled through the window without leaving the warmth of the living room fire.

As for those old fashioned crumbs! Phooey! Birds now demand equal rights with the local D.P.A. No crumbs, thank you. We'll have choice, mixed wild bird seed or better yet, the finest hybrid sunflower seeds. Failing to obtain such the feeder may supply crushed peanuts or even peanut butter.

You see, it's no longer a matter of charity. It's out and out competition. Question is who can attract the largest numbers and varieties of those feathered chiselers. If my neighbor seems to be getting the greater number, I'll just have to set a better table and beat him. If he gets ten cardinals I must get at least twelve with a blue jay or two for good measure. If he attracts eight varieties I must get a dozen if I have to import them.

Don't think this won't run into good money. Bird feeding, like all sports, is now commercialized. Every grocery store seems to handle a variety of bird seeds. And not just a few, mind you, one store in a small town sold 1,600 pounds of bird seed in one winter. Chain stores in bigger places likely sell more. We fork over a dollar for five pounds of seed and never bat an eye. Sunflower seeds come as high as two pounds for sixty-nine cents, but the big economy five-pound bag can be bought for less than a buck. In short, millions of dollars annually start on their happy little merry-go-round because millions of people like to watch those cheerful little gluttons put on the feed bag.

This part I hate to mention, but I must do it. Like all other branches of sports, bird feeding seems to have attracted a few of the untruthful boys. They may be those who are really fishermen and just fill in the winter months feeding birds. Anyhow, when a dozen bird feeders get together the tall tales fly thick and fast. Everyone tops the other guy's story and first man doesn't even have a chance. Before the session ends the world is covered with birds and every man of the bunch knows that all the others are liars.

All this competitive activity is a boon to the bird life. Those little bums sure do cash in on the deal. They know every bird feeder in each community and know just what sort of table he sets. They either place the stamp of approval on a station by eating there or they desert it with cool disdain. They really get downright snooty about the whole deal. After all why should they take second rate feed when by thirty seconds of flight they can get better?

In my town where I'm one of the biggest of the suckers, the much sought after bird is the evening grosbeak. Those big yellow, black and white fellows are the exotic elite and they know it. They know all feeders want them and they cash in on their popularity. They may taste of your various brands of food in a disdainful way but if you want to keep them it's sunflower seed you'd better get and plenty of it.

During this past winter, I've made myself the biggest sucker in my community by spending around ten dollars for sunflower seeds alone. My reward is that I have between fifty and a hundred evening grosbeaks as steady boarders, along with such old friends as cardinals, nuthatches, chickadees, jays, starlings, woodpeckers and three or four varieties of sparrows. A lone dove spent a week with me and a few others drop in occasionally. However, the grosbeaks have hogged the show as well as the food supply.

The grosbeak made his first appearance here only a few years ago. At that time the theory was advanced that he had moved from his northern home due to failure of certain foods there. Now, however, the boys who are in on the secret of birds tell me that the bird is extending his range. Anyhow we've had them every winter ever since the first appearance.

Somebody must be checking on the movements of the grosbeak. No fewer than four that board with me are wearing leg bands. We've caught two of these and sent the numbers to Washington. One was banded January 29, 1958, at State College, Pennsylvania, the other April 14, 1961, at South Londonderry, Vermont.

How did we catch the bird? Here's where eyebrows may rise. My wife and I simply placed a shelf outside the window and placed sunflower seeds on it. They found the new place in less than an hour. Within five days they were eating from our extended hands and coming into the kitchen to feed among the potted plants on my wife's flower table. When a banded bird entered, a sudden movement caused him to fly upward and miss the open window. It was then easy to pluck the bird from the window curtains. Such an experience didn't seem to bother the bird much. Next day they were, as usual, on the shelf for their handouts.

To sum up this rambling, I don't think I've saved many bird lives this winter. Maybe I've helped put a lot on B.D.P.A. and kept others too fat to fly north again. At least I've enjoyed feeding the bums and the time my wife put in watching them might otherwise have been spent studying catalogs. (Any husband knows how costly catalog studies can be.) So if you're looking for a new pastime, buy a fancy feeder or make one, get a big supply of bird seed, suet, bread crumbs, etc., and try feeding birds.

****

LET'S WATCH THE FIGHTS

The human race seems to enjoy fights—that is as long as someone else is doing the fisticuffs. Just let half a dozen people sit down before the great God television and hear how many say, "Let's watch the fights." A good part of the group are usually in favor of watching two guys maul each other and the better the beating, the said two guys give each other, the better the audience likes it. I suppose we are the only species that like a fight purely for the sake of fighting.

Animals and birds of nature's kingdom are different. They fight. In fact, they put on some royal battles. The difference is that they have reasons for the scrap.

What are the reasons? There are many. Leading the list is perhaps the fight for a mate. When the old procreation urge hits nature's "chilluns" you can expect some real contests. These, of course, are mostly among the males. The human race in modern days finds more women fighting over men than vice versa.

One of the most savage fights I ever witnessed was between two male skunks. I was attracted to the scene of the battle by the squeals and growls of the contestants. When I came near I found the two in deadly combat. Near at hand the female, for whose favor the battle raged, was coyly watching.

Both males were mud plastered and bedraggled, for it was on a rainy morning. They were at each other tooth and claw, with a savage fury that indicated death for the other was the sole aim of each. Both dirty coats were liberally smeared with blood and tufts of hair littered the ground. Neither showed any sign of weakening. They would draw apart for two or three feet and then come together in a kicking, clawing, squealing tangle. If one got a good mouthful of his opponent, he would shake and twist him in perfect bulldog manner until his hold tore loose.

Occasionally there would, as if by common consent, be a lull in the fight and the opponents would draw apart. Then one or the other would start toward the female. That would be the signal for the other to tie into him with the ferocity of a tiger. This happened four or five times while I watched them.

At no time during the forty-five minutes that I watched did either one threaten to use his scent weapon. Perhaps it's no good against kinfolks. Then while the two were engaged in perhaps the twentieth tangle, the female quietly slipped into a hole in a rocky bank. Whereupon, both males ceased to battle and began a hurried but rather aimless search for the lady, which took both out of my sight.

Evidently other animals fight with greater savagery when there's a lady in the case. A female dog in heat frequently results in a battle to the death among neighborhood dogs. Each year we find mute testimony to the fact that two bucks will fight to a finish for a doe.

An eight-point buck, found dead near my hometown, had more than a hundred punctures in his sides and the torn up area, where the battle had raged, was of about a quarter acre in extent. No one knows how much the winner had suffered, but his tracks leading away from the place were bloody.

Animals fight for food territory. That's the simple law of survival. Too many mouths to feed means lean feeding. Instinct tells them to get rid of opposition.

Perhaps one of the oldest forms of conflict in the animal world is the battling of a mother against her young. Somehow nature gets the fact across that the young must scatter or there will be inbreeding of the species. When they are ready to go she says "go" and means it. A mother red squirrel will be a solicitous thing until her young are grown then she turns on them with a fury that sends them packing.

A mother bear may have her cubs with her the second year, but then it's time to go. With good sound cuffs the youngsters

219

are speeded on their way. Foxes drive off the young ones the first year. Here it is worthy of note to observe that silver foxes, a result of inbreeding among the reds, have been found in greatest numbers on some of our northern islands. Perhaps here the young could not go so far away and the result was more inbreeding.

Animals fight for supremacy in the herd, flock or family. It is not only for vanity either. Once a fellow member has been soundly whipped, he'll give ground where food is to be found. That old peck system goes for the smallest birds and for animals as big as the bison.

We find little conflict between animals of different species, unless of course, one is an object of prey to the other. With two rival meat eaters like the fox and wildcat there is not likely to be trouble. One species will yield to the other without a test fight.

I must mention here the most stupid fight I ever witnessed. It was between two large snapping turtles. Why they were fighting I don't know. They were both well-meaning turtles and battled with great enthusiasm. Their wicked heads hit each other with impacts that sounded like two rocks coming together. The trouble was that I couldn't see any damage being done. Both were so well armored and kept themselves so well protected that the whole battle was useless. Maybe they both claimed a moral victory, but I couldn't see one drop of blood on either one.

Territory plays an important part in nature's fights. A male bird maps out a nesting territory because he can usually drive away any other male of the species. Or could it be that the visitor does not fight well on unfamiliar ground? It must be that way with dogs.

Years ago I used to take my rabbit dog of mixed ancestry around a certain farm on hunting trips. If the farmer's dog saw us on his territory, he invariably came out and whipped my dog. Then each time the farmer came to town with his dog following him, my dog would go out to the road and pick a fight. He always whipped the farm dog.

I suppose it is only natural to assume that all animals are born with the instinct to fight. I can't think of a better place to observe this than with a litter of newborn pigs. When only a few hours old the little fellows will put on some good sham battles. The interesting part is that two of them will stand up to each other with heads lapping and go through the motions of cutting each other to ribbons with an upward thrust of the lower jaws. All they lack is that big tusk which was the property of their wild ancestors. They have lost the tusk, thanks to modern agriculture, but they haven't lost the method of using it.

****

TREE OF THE CROSS

The beautiful old legend of the dogwood tree tells us that the cross upon which Christ was crucified was made of dogwood, then a fine big upright tree. Because of the grief of the tree at being used for such a base purpose it was granted to the dogwood that it ever after grow low and gnarled and unsuited to making crosses. In addition its flowers should forever be in the form of the cross.

Now I'm not laying claim to being a maker of legends but I think there could well be another one in tribute to the thorn tree. Somehow, I'd like to think that the thorn was unwilling that her spines be used to pierce the brow of our Master. For her reward it could well be that she was granted the power to grow and thrive under almost any condition of soil, altitude or climate. In addition the twisted branches could have been decreed the feeding station of thousands.

If my modern legend is no good, at least let each hunter remove his battered or new hat as he passes by the humble thorn tree. It is truly the meal ticket of many thousands of nature's children. Furthermore, it is not hardtack rations to them. Rather it is the eagerly sought delicacy for which many plainer foods are passed up.

Throughout the Allegheny ranges and far into the lowlands the persistent thorn pushes its way. It is not particular. On high windswept mountains you may find ancient thorns. Their branches are twisted by the storms of winter and twined thickly together as if to seek the support of each other. Their roots clutch the rocky soil like talon fingers, finding a hold in a convenient crack or beneath huge boulders.

Down on the moist bottomlands we find the thorn in thickets and groves. There they grow taller and more graceful but lose the appearance of tough durability seen in those of the bare

221

mountaintops. In all places between the two levels, wherever a bird may have dropped a seed the hardy thorn may be found. Against all enemies, and against man in particular, it wages a stubborn fight and wins. Its very appearance suggests a rugged fighter that asks no odds and needs none.

Thorn trees may be reasonably mature at fifty years. They may live another fifty, hardy, tough years bearing heavy crops and holding their sturdy appearance to the end.

We seldom see a partially dead thorn. Usually they live in all their hardy stubbornness to the end and when they die they die all over. Once dead they disappear quickly, leaving no trace of their existence.

Against the low growing and close branched thorn, winds are almost powerless. Clutching roots hold fiercely to the soil and rocks. The knotty wood of trunk and branches holds defiantly against the strongest storms and the tree comes through unscratched. To see one uprooted or broken is a rarity.

In the fall of the year the thorn tree is in its glory. Every branch bears its load of thorn apples, yellow or red according to its particular variety. In size the fruits may vary from one-fourth to one-half inch in diameter: they fall from the branches in such numbers as to carpet the ground beneath or to fill each pocket on steep hillsides.

Then it is that the banquet season starts. Mother Nature's children hear the cry "soup's on" and they turn out by thousands.

For a number of years now I have studied the "boarding house of the thorn" and have found some surprising facts. I don't even pretend to think that I've yet uncovered all.

What creatures devour the thorn apple? The answer is just about everything that walks or flies and wears hair or feathers. First comes the grand old man of the forest—the bear. He won't even wait for the fall drop. As soon as the fruits are ripe he's busy tearing at the branches. Until hibernation puts him to his long sleep he'll continue to visit the thorn thickets.

Along with the bear comes the deer. To them the thorn is such a specialty that it is not uncommon to find the ground beneath a tree bare of grass or weed growth. Deer have destroyed the cover in gathering up the last little apple.

Turkeys know each thorn tree of their range and visit them on each round. At the tree they compete with grouse for those that have fallen and fly into the thorny branches for more.

During the night the trees may be visited by rabbits, raccoons, opossums, skunks, foxes, muskrats, mice, woodrats and of course domestic animals like the cow, horse and sheep. With all these the thorn apple is not merely a passing nibble or light lunch. It is an eagerly sought and staple food.

Maybe you doubt the number I've listed. Maybe you are one who thinks of foxes, skunks, opossums and coons as meat eaters only. You couldn't miss it farther. Each one of these chaps really puts away a pile of vegetables and fruit-type groceries. In fact they may in the course of a year eat far more such foods than they do meat. Foxes, skunks and opossums go for almost any type of berry or fruit. The coon does likewise and adds mast to the list.

The thorn fruit being high on the preferred list keeps such animals near the thorn thickets. The rabbit, for example, may remain close to a thorn tree throughout a deep snow and live happily by digging up the little apples.

All of the other mentioned will dig through several inches of snow to find thorn apples. This brings up another feature. While many of the fruits do rot in a fairly short time many will keep unharmed for an entire winter. I have raked them out of the dried leaves in early spring as bright cheeked as they were in the fall.

In time of mast shortage all varieties of squirrels will thrive on thorn apples. They eat both fruit and seeds. On one morning in March I observed three red squirrels and a rabbit busily digging thorn apples from beneath a big tree that stands in my front yard. All four of them had practically wintered there.

The story is not yet complete. Thorn apples are borne in great quantities and many are not eaten. Therefore, like any other fruit, many rot under the trees. Now come the quail and song birds along with the grouse and turkey. Until the last seed is eaten the tree is still a popular feeding station. You may find turkeys working under a thorn tree as late as June. Those seeds are still good.

All in all I doubt very much that any other variety of tree can claim to feed the number of wild creatures that the thorn provides for. Neither can any boast of keeping its boarders for such a long period of the year.

****

UNTO THE HILLS

From where I have lived most all my life I can look westward through a notch in the hills and see the great bulk of Cheat Mountain shoulder out the sky. For more than half a century, I have watched the sun drop behind the same mountain at the end of day. During winter days I have "lifted up mine eyes unto the hills" from a snow free valley to see Cheat shouldered in white. From across the lofty top has come the black clouds that brought rain, hail or snow to our valley, and down from its top have swept the cold winds of winter that chilled me to the bone.

Other things have come from Cheat. The exciting tales of prowess in the lumber woods that thrilled me as a boy. The big black bears that were brought in by the hunters; the bobcats and turkeys; the huge buckets of tangy blackberries and the brightly colored brook trout came from that mystical mountain.

Down from Cheat came the big Shay engines bearing their long trails of log cars. With them came big "wood hicks" for weekends in town. Their red checked "Richie" shirts, the brand of their trade, made colorful splashes on the streets of our town. The notches cut around their hat brims showed how many days they had worked. Their "cutter shoes" studded with "corks" punched holes in sidewalks and store floors, and occasionally punched wicked holes in the bodies of two fighting hicks.

Down from Cheat came the stories I loved. The tales about deer, unknown then in lower regions, made my eyes glow. There were stories of Herculean feats in the woods, stories of fights, stories of deep snows and fifty below zero cold. Accounts of accidents, train wrecks and killings made Cheat a fabled land for a boy.

There were tall stories too. Tales of mosquitos that ate all the meat off one side of a logger and then brought a cant hook to turn him over. There were rats so big they were caught trying on the loggers' clothes. There were graybacks so big the hicks used them for trout bait when they fished Cheat River. The

224

men in those camps could eat a quarter of beef at a sitting and top it off with a gallon of coffee. Men made drinks of accumulated prune juice so potent it sometimes blew up the cookhouses. There were big peace-loving men "who never started a fight, but finished a hell of a lot of them."

Yes, Cheat was a fabulous place; a place where giants moved; a place where romance existed; a place where snowshoe rabbits lived and big hoot owls moved through the tops of swaying spruce trees. It was a land that created legends, and a land that fired the imagination of all the boys in my town.

Today all the human element is changed. The hoarse whistle of the big Shay is heard only in memory. The "corked" shoes of the hicks cut no holes in the boardwalks. No trains of logs snake down the steep slopes with their brakes so tight that fire flies from every wheel. We hear no mention of "Camp 27," or "old 19." Supply cars no longer run to supply hungry loggers. The great "Company Store" is closed and silent. The whine of the saw is still. The logger of a thousand fabled tales is seen no more.

Yet Cheat in all its awesome bulk still stands as before. Civilization has made no inroads upon it. It is wilderness now as it was then. The black bear still lumbers through its woods. The wildcat still hunts the snowshoe hare and the big owls still glide on silent wings to and fro. Cheat River still chuckles over the stones and still holds the brightly colored trout. New spruce forests blanket the land and furnish a home for deer, turkeys and other creatures of the wild.

Cheat, rising 4,500 feet and more, is still as one logger said, "A piece of Canada gone astray." The high forest assumes all the characteristics of the far northern woods. Here thrive the spruce, beech, white birch, and other trees of the northland. Down under the trees the forest floor is true Canadian. The mosses, weeds, flowers and shrubs are those of the colder land. Here the visitor can find himself in a new world of nature with a two-hour climb. By that climb he may leave the central hardwood region with its oak, maple, poplar, walnut and other deciduous trees and find himself treading the deep moss floor of the big evergreen northern forest. The change is so complete as to give one the feeling of being in another world.

In the fall and early winter one may leave a region of earth covered with the crisp brown leaves of autumn. When he reaches the top of Cheat he may enter a fairyland of ice and snow. He may follow Cheat River, now dumb, its voice stilled by ice. He may leave tracks in one or two feet of snow as he looks in wonder at the ice sheathed trees. The vapor of the high top keeps that ice film on every trunk and branch for many weeks of each winter.

While on his trip he may track or even sight the elusive bear or graceful deer. Bobcat tracks will crisscross the huge pad marks of snowshoe hares. The hiker may find a bloody patch of snow where the big cat leaped upon an unsuspecting hare or even find where a deer has been pulled down to death by one of the hungry cats. When evening comes the visitor may drop back down the steep slopes and again stand on dry autumn leaves in a warmer valley where the icy finger of winter has not yet destroyed autumn color.

Yes, that romantic mountain of my boyhood is still there. It waits for those who would see it in all its moods and with all its changing faces. Someday it will be a tourist mecca. Someday one-half the population of the United States will know it lies but a day or less of driving from their own homes. Its fame and legends will spread. It will be known far and wide.

How long? Not until West Virginia wakes up and tells the world it's there. When will that be? I don't know, but soon I hope.—Reprinted by permission of Earl L. Core, editor, *Natural History of the Cass Scenic Railroad*

****

BIRD FISHERMEN

During the summer days when the young man's fancy (as well as the old man's and everybody else's) lightly turns to thoughts of fish, we often hear envious remarks concerning the fishing skill of some local Ike Walton. We hear that Joe So and So is an expert with flies while Jim Somebody "drags 'em in wholesale with baits." Top guy is the one who, "can catch fish where there ain't any." (Why shouldn't he? He has far more water to fish than anyone else.)

Top fishermen in my book of wonder and envy are some of nature's birds. I envy them because unlike me they seem never to fail. I wonder about them because I simply can't figure out how they do it.

I can come nearest to understanding the divers such as loon and grebe. I've been underwater with limited skin diving equipment and find that when a man is totally underwater fish show little fear. In fact they cruise about in a rather unconcerned manner. In the clear water around the Bahama Islands I could almost enclose some very colorful fish in my hands. They seemed little concerned with my presence. A diving bird with his fast movements should have little trouble making a catch.

It seems that what alarms fish is commotion on the surface or just above it. Our big blue herons and other long-legged waders are next easiest to reconcile. Standing as motionless as the stump he may appear like he offers no betraying movement to frighten fish. When an unsuspecting victim comes within range the dart of his pointed beak is really fast and accurate. He seldom misses his lunch. With the wader, patience pays off and he depends upon it. Even so, he's got to be darn fast.

Many times I've seen fish of varied kinds lying just under the surface of the water. This is often noticed in still backwaters or land-locked pools. In such still water fish apparently rise to the warmer water at the surface. For experiment I've tried sailing a rock across those schools. When the rock passes over, the disappearance of the fish is unbelievably fast. In a split second every one is gone, leaving only ripples to show where they had been. It's going to take a fast bird to nail a fish before it can dart to safety.

All of which makes me wonder mightily about our properly named kingfishers. From a perch anywhere from four to twenty feet above the water he studies the pool below. When his victim is spotted he launches himself into a dive. I've watched him do it a hundred times. Never did the dive seem so fast. The entry into the water is not a beautiful swan dive but more of an awkward plop. Yet never on more than two or three occasions have I seen a kingfisher come up without a fish.

How does he do it? I throw a rock over a school of minnows or larger fish with what seems far greater speed than the kingfisher musters and the fish are gone before the rock strikes. Yet Mr. and Mrs. Kingfisher continue to dive with monotonous regularity and to wing away after each dive with a fish for those

227

young fishermen stowed in a nest at the back of a ten to twenty-foot tunnel somewhere along the river bank.

The greatest marvel of all to me is the big osprey or fish hawk. That big six-foot wingspread surely doesn't look like fast fishing equipment but his entire diet is made up of fish. Some say he catches only suckers and other rough fish but no dice. I've seen one catch a bass and have removed flesh of bass from the stomachs of others brought to me for mounting. A bass is a fast mover anyway you take him. I've watched the osprey dive for fish many times. Most of the time he spots his prey from a convenient perch in a tree, but twice I've seen the big boy drop into the water from flight. I have never seen one miss getting his fish. I suppose they do, on occasion, miss but they've always been perfect under my observance.

Now, how does he do it? When he drops into the water he actually appears awkward. He makes a big splash and creates a big disturbance. When he comes to the surface and takes off he gives the impression that he fell in and had a tough time getting out. However, he usually has his fish clutched in those big talons when he rises. The fish are not minnows either. A two-pound sucker is an ordinary catch.

Once when I was fishing a long, still eddy on the Greenbrier a big osprey came flapping his way upstream. His flight was slow and rather lazy and he was cruising at a full fifty feet above the water. When directly in front of me he folded his wings and dropped. He hit the water with a resounding splash and was under for a matter of five seconds or more. When he arose he carried a sucker about eighteen inches long. Everything about the incident looked wrong. The drop seemed slow. The strike on the surface was accompanied by a loud splash. The water there was deep, which should have allowed the sucker a good chance to escape. The only thing that looked right was the fact that he got his fish.

I don't believe a bird can hypnotize a fish nor paralyze one with fright. Charming is out. There's not time for that. Maybe some day someone will tell me how in the devil he does it. Until that time I'll just wonder and envy those experts in feathers.

****

WHO IS HE?

Every time I pick up a paper I find that we are observing or asking for observance of some certain week. I find such worthy weeks as fire prevention week, be kind to mud turtles week, dairy products week, safety week and the like. Now I'm going to ask for . . . not one week, but two weeks for a famed gentleman that I know.

My gentleman needs a thorough and positive identification. We must know him. We must never forget him. Forget Honest Abe and G. Washington if you must. Pull Hannibal out of the Alps with all his elephants. Send Napoleon, Hitler and Khrushchev to the limbo of forgotten dictators, but never forget my candidate for the eternal halls of fame.

All of us who go afield with rod and gun will meet him. Rest assured of that. Identification, however, may be a trifle difficult for the tyro. Here are the marks. By these signs you shall know him.

He will likely be dressed in clothes similar to those worn by a common everyday sportsman. He's a great mimic and loves to appear as what he is not, so you'll have no help in recognition through clothing. You'll have to look for other points.

The gent will carry a gun much like that of the sportsman. About the only difference will be that it is bigger, spreads a wider shot pattern, holds more ammunition and shoots faster than others.

At this point let me advise you to stay in open woods when hunting. If you meet my hall of fame candidate while you are moving a bush, your greeting will be a load of buckshot. He never takes chances. He always shoots first, looks afterwards. No use letting game escape.

When you meet him in open woods you'll note his easy familiarity with the woods. He's been there before—that is, before the season opened. During your first few words of conversation you'll hear much profanity and damning of all officials because little stocking has been done. You'll also get a leer and a behind the hand remark that he got 38 squirrels there before the season opened. He'll add information to the effect that there would be

229

game left if "that bunch of damn outlaws from the other side of the crick hadn't sneaked in and killed everything."

About this time you may notice that his game coat is rather bulky. In your own naive way you may ask how near the limit he is. Again you'll get the leer and be informed, "May have the state limit but ain't got *my* limit yet."

By now you may be mildly suspicious that you've met my gentleman. Wait a minute.

The next conversational gems will likely be to the effect that he "may as well get 'em," because if he doesn't "some of them other fellers will."

Should your encounter be in deer season you'll hear, "Can't eat horns." Or "What are we after, horns or meat?" Better yet you may hear, "Ain't checked my first one yet. May get another." All these are more confirming proofs that you've met my candidate for two special weeks.

Next step is to maneuver yourself directly in front of the suspected specimen. (Don't get too close. He gives off a terrible odor.) Now look him squarely in the face. If he is the boy you are looking for both jowls will hang down rather low in a peculiarly suggestive manner. The nose and mouth will both protrude far in advance of the rest of the face. However, the eyes will be the dead give away. They'll be deep sunken and very piggish in appearance.

If you have verified all the above features you are ready for next to the last test. Just lay your gun down and pretend not to be watching it. Since he's already *stealing your game* chances are he'll try to steal your gun. If he does, identification is almost complete.

Now try the final test. Grab him suddenly from behind. (You can wash off later at the nearest stream.) Holding him firmly, jerk his shirt tail out and push it clear up to his neck. Look quickly at his spinal region. There you'll see a prominent row of coarse bristles. These will run from the back of his neck down to the region you'd like to kick into a bottomless ravine. Identification is now complete. You've met the All-American Game Hog.

Now why do I want two weeks set aside for this obnoxious big brother to the skunk? Simple. I want two weeks open season on him; two full weeks not excluding Sundays, during which any honest hunter may shoot, trap, chase, pursue with

230

the intent to kill, or otherwise do physical harm to the Great American Game Hog. I would not exclude any type of lethal firearm. Above all, spotlighting would not only be acceptable but widely encouraged. The limit per hunter should be about twelve a season.

Just in case my request is granted by the powers that be, I'd like to add a few notes on hunting the varmints.

1. Slip into the woods a few days before the season opens. You should have seven or eight hung up before opening day.

2. Don't check your kill until the last day of hunting season. By such a simple device, you may get by with two season limits.

3. As soon as you get one, hide him and go on hunting. Tell other hunters you haven't got your limit yet.

4. Use heavy guns with many shells and a wide pattern.

5. Last and above all get a good spotlight. Those little piggish eyes will gleam like diamonds in a light ray.

And the best of luck be with you.

Photographs by Wayne Cox

I've fished a brawling mountain brook,
   W. E. Blackhurst, "An Evening Prayer"
   Afterglow, page 140

233